✒ THE ANTIQUE COLLECTOR'S GUIDE TO STYLES AND PRICES

Rita Reif

THE ANTIQUE COLLECTOR'S GUIDE TO STYLES AND PRICES

Hawthorn Books, Inc.   *Publishers*   *New York*

THE ANTIQUE COLLECTOR'S GUIDE TO STYLES AND PRICES

To Paul, Leslie, and Timothy,
the best parts of the four-leaf clover

Acknowledgments

I wish to express my sincere appreciation to all those who have so generously assisted me in the gathering of the illustrative material for this book. In particular, I wish to thank Mary Vandegrift, Anne Hochgraf, and Walthena Slaughter, of Parke-Bernet Galleries, without whom this book would never have been completed. I am also indebted to Dr. Donald Shelley, Robert G. Wheeler, and Mrs. C. V. Hagler, of The Henry Ford Museum and Greenfield Village, Dearborn, Michigan; to Arthur Drexler, Elizabeth Shaw, and Richard Tooke, of the Museum of Modern Art, New York City; to Charlotte La Rue, of the Museum of the City of New York; to Ruth Larner, of the Pilgrim Society, Plymouth, Massachusetts. Although it is not possible to thank each dealer in turn for so patiently aiding in this effort, I am deeply appreciative for the careful attention all gave to my inquiries. To Mary Osborne and the staff of the Eastern States Antiques Fair, a special vote of thanks.

CONTENTS ॐ

II: AMERICA

INTRODUCTION

◆§ Is a Louis XV poudreuse a better investment than a blue-chip stock? Can a milking stool from an old New England barn bring a bigger return than bonds? Will French eighteenth-century furnishings, like Man o' War, race on and on, always after the high stakes, breaking all records in the current antiques boom?

Supposedly the answers to these questions have been contained in news stories, terse televised programs and the flood of optimistic intelligence issued periodically by auction houses on the subject.

"Antique Prices Soar as Supplies Dwindle," proclaimed *The New York Times* in a front-page headline on January 29, 1966. What was thought to be phase two in the "going, going, gone" process three years ago is still going. Going upward, indeed. But far from gone.

All this publicity about inflated prices and scarcities in Early American high-boys and Hepplewhite sideboards is true, but only partially so. Too often the high-priced examples cited are the plums of the antiques market, the major contenders for floor space in museums. When escalating sales figures on furnishings are given, the bottom sum noted is frequently one registered during the depths of the 1930's depression. Or the record lows are for furnishings that were out of fashion then and have since ascended in the public's affections.

The fact is that there are period pieces for every palate and, in most cases, prices to match almost every pocketbook. And the stepped-up pace in auction houses and antiques shops has shown that there are qualities and styles just waiting to be snapped up by collectors, if not investors.

Today's spiraling prices on antiques might well be compared to a three-stage rocket. Prices for the least valuable or fashionable antiques climb only so high before breaking away. The middle of the market soars on until it, too, levels off, leaving the finest antiques, like the Apollo capsule, hurtling through the stratosphere heading toward the moon.

Just how high sales figures in some styles have risen thus far in the current boom is documented on the following pages. But the emphasis is not on top market prices. It is on moderate and budget purchases. And, of course, collectors should not expect to be able to exactly duplicate the sales figures in their shopping. The prices given are intended as guidelines. They may waver in any direction. And the careful collector will certainly try to do better in making acquisitions.

But price is not the only, or the most important, consideration in buying antiques at a price. Judgments on style, quality, proportion, craftsmanship and suitability will be made. Hopefully the information contained here will assist in making those decisions.

Most important of all, any discussion of period furnishings automatically involves history. Thus there is a cursory survey on the pages below of the times that shaped each furniture style—times during which political, economic, social and æsthetic forces determined a change in the shape of a leg or the wood used in a table. It is in this aspect of the decorative arts that the collecting mystique is best understood.

RITA REIF

part I

EUROPE

chapter 1

GOTHIC THROUGH ELIZABETHAN

~§ The term "Gothic" was a slur Italians applied to the style that reigned supreme through most of Europe during the later Middle Ages. From the twelfth through the sixteenth centuries architects and artists spun mortar, stone, stained glass, threads and wood into one of the most spiritual expressions in art that the world has ever seen.

The one country where Gothic never took hold was Italy. There the style was considered barbaric, created by descendants of the Goths of the North. It was an art expression that flouted the classical principles to which Italy held fast. The land destined to retain the style longer than any other was England, where vestiges lingered into the seventeenth century.

Gothic was also the art of the people. It was the common people who built the cathedrals, those architectural monuments that fully characterize the tightly woven fabric of life in which God was the warp, the church the woof of their existence. Gothic is at once crude and æsthetic, solid and mysteriously aloof, direct and inspiring.

A fixed order existed in society and in the arts, with architecture reigning supreme and all other arts subordinate to it. The art movement began on the Île-de-France in the twelfth century and spread with variations to Germany, the Nordic lands, and across the Channel to England. If the architecture was an encyclopedia of ornament in stone, the furniture was its parallel in wood. Chairs, tables, credences (chests) hewn into strong, simple forms that were as vertical in character as the spires of Chartres, were carved with graceful, lace-like motifs, intertwining tracery, linenfold and diaper patterns.

Furniture was a great luxury in this period. Only the nobles could afford to own the few articles necessary for their basic needs. With the exception of storage cupboards, everything was designed to be easily transported within a castle or from one castle to another. This portable aspect explains the French and Italian words for furniture—*meubles* and *mobili,* which mean "movables."

Trestle tables, with two or three carved slab supports, had thick rectangular tops that were removed after each feast and stored away to clear the great hall for dancing, entertaining or sleeping guests.

Chairs were either high-backed, slab-sided, box-based throne chairs or simple backless stools with X-shaped bases that folded easily. They were used for dining or sitting everywhere in the castle and could be packed up and carried away by the princes of the realm to their other castles as the seasons changed or the king commanded.

Trestle benches, with or without backs, were also used at table and along the walls of the great hall. Tripod-based chairs, which were far easier to make and more secure to sit on in castles with uneven floors, were also favored. Four-legged chairs were not used widely until the Renaissance.

The leather, fabric-covered, or plain wood chests were boxes with flat or rounded tops that stored linens, clothing, cooking utensils and jewels. Many were flat on the bottom to make them more functional as traveling trunks. The carrying handles at each side and the elaborately worked iron locks in front made them eminently functional and safe for moving a noble's possessions when the retinue of his household embarked on a journey.

Beds with carved head, foot and sideboards, standing on blocklike legs, could likewise be dismantled for travel—that is, unless the bed was built into the wall. Frigid bedrooms in northern climes made it necessary to hang several layers of curtaining over the one open side or to enclose the bed with wood doors or leather panels.

Only the built-in beds and the cupboards were left behind, and the latter were often the crudest of all furnishings. They were either too heavy or too primitive to tempt marauders to steal them in a noble's absence.

Right: Gothic choir stall has pierced Gothic tracery in overhead panels on back and base. Linenfold panels under arms end in square, block legs. *French and Company*

Below: Flat-topped oak coffer was equipped with side and top handles for traveling. The strength and richness of the mid fifteenth-century Gothic style is evident in the square feet carved with rosettes and shell motifs and the wrought iron mounts—strappings binding top, sides and base— the pierced hasp and lockplate and the quatrefoil terminations. *Parke-Bernet Galleries*

The cultivated court life of the late Middle Ages, when chivalry was developed to its highest form, encouraged colorful decorations in the castles of France and to a lesser extent in Flanders, Germany and England. Many of the cupboards were painted in bright reds, blues, and golds—colors that dominate the palettes of painters of the period. Since these furnishings were sometimes built into the walls of a room, it has been assumed that the woodwork also was often painted in vivid hues. But the extant paneling remaining in most of the castles from the period or appearing today in museums or homes of antiques collectors is most often without color. Paintings from the period often show the rich, dark wood—the walnut and oak—without any gilding or color.

Painted or not, the Gothic furniture had its decorative side in the elaborate carvings that covered the façades of credences, the surfaces of high-backed chairs, bed frames, and the front, side and top panels of chests. Elongated diaper patterns enclosing flowers ran up the sides of bedposts. Linenfold, an exercise in carving that tested an artisan's wits in chiseling an amazing variety of ways in which fabric folds could be represented, embellished chests, credences, chair backs and sides, and bed frames. Pierced perpendicular tracery, shaped like windows of Gothic cathedrals, decorated the façades of food cupboards. Rosettes dotted the panels of storage pieces.

Pierced and carved panels form a distinctive façade on this sturdy Gothic oak food cupboard. The pierced work, modeled after details in the windows of European cathedrals, served the practical purpose of ventilation. *Parke-Bernet Galleries*

Occasionally the front panels of small boxes were carved with biblical or jousting scenes. Many such designs bore the initials of the owner and the year that the pieces were made. The vertical character of most of the carving and decoration on Gothic furniture does indeed emulate the feeling of the spired architecture of the period. But Gothic chairs rarely echo the silhouette of a church spire as they would in the eighteenth- and nineteenth-century neo-Gothic periods in the hands of Chippendale and later cabinetmakers. This distinction in the form, as well as the primitive construction techniques of the period, makes it easy to separate the early furniture from the later interpretations.

One exception to this is the fourteenth-century coronation chair that stands in Edward the Confessor's Chapel, in Westminster Abbey in London. The spire-shaped back, flanked by pinnacles, may well have served as a model for the neo-Gothic adaptations. But this throne chair is unique. For the most part, chairs have flat, not pointed top rails, or curved wood canopies.

Carpenters were the medieval furniture makers up to the middle of the fourteenth century when joinery was rediscovered. Although the Egyptians are known to have used joinery as early as 1380 B.C., the craft was forgotten in medieval Europe. Gothic joinery is the woodworking method by which wood parts are put together by mortise and tenon—the mortise being the cavity into which the tenon projection fits—and are secured by pegs or dowels.

Later, dovetail joints, as well as tongue-and-groove joinery methods, were developed in woodworking. The Gothic joiners were considered fine craftsmen, and the furniture they made was lighter, used less wood and was therefore less expensive to make. It was also easier to transport than the work of carpenters.

Few Gothic furnishings are extant in today's world. The designs that did exist in comparatively great numbers as late as the early twentieth century have since disappeared into museums or great private collections.

Before and through the boom years of the 1920's the titans of industry such as J. P. Morgan, William Randolph Hearst, Joseph Widener, Henry Clay Frick, Philip Lehman and a host of others vied with one another over the purchase of French and German Gothic cabinets and chests, paying $30,000 and more for such rare pieces.

In the 1930's collectors could still find an occasional chest or credence at an auction or in antiques establishments that specialized in early furniture. These were most often pieces that had been collected by the American men of wealth in earlier decades of the century. Following their deaths, or the loss of their fortunes and homes during the depression, their collections were broken up and sold or dispersed.

But as fashion and fancies dictated, the style was no longer popular at the close of World War II, when the new generation of industrial tycoons set about furnishing their homes. Occasionally in the 1950's one found modest pieces for a fraction of the cost that they had brought thirty years earlier. A chest with linenfold paneling cost $300 and up. A rare four-poster bed was $500. A Gothic choir stall was $200. But the finest examples of Gothic furniture stood like silent sentinels in the warehouses of one or two dealers bearing their pre-1929 price tags.

The Gothic mode lived longer in England than in any other country, continuing into the sixteenth century, well over one hundred years after the Renaissance had unseated the earlier style. The boxlike, high-backed chairs or stalls of the Gothic era continued to be made with linenfold paneling, sometimes united with such Italian Renaissance motifs as medallion, gadroon, acanthus and figural forms.

The Gothic joint stool became more commonplace in sixteenth-century English castles than it had been a century earlier in French and German palaces. For if the English were slow to import the Renaissance style, they were faster in responding to the continental standards of comfort, luxury and refinement in living.

One of the most typical of all Tudor elements in furniture is the bulbous leg appearing on court, hall and parlor cupboards, beds and the massive dining tables of the Elizabethan period. The form is like a medieval, pedestal-based drinking vessel and is often called melon-shaped. The top part corresponding to the cup cover of a goblet is sometimes covered with gadrooning, the base with acanthus leaves. The leg actually derives from German and Flemish table legs but was developed further in the hands of the English and the Italian craftsmen who were brought by Tudor monarchs to London to introduce some of the continental fashions to their castles.

Elizabethan furniture was generally of oak, although some walnut was used. The use of inlay became known, probably through the presence of Italian craftsmen on the London scene. But most inlaid squarish chests were more medieval in silhouette and motifs of decoration than Renaissance. Medieval scenes were worked into façades, showing castles and knights and some trompe l'oeil effects. Heraldry was also documented by wood-carvers. They also employed many Renaissance elements such as masks, grotesques and some classical motifs, but rarely in such a pure manner that would make it possible to mistake a London chest for one made earlier in Florence.

Beds of the Elizabethan age were massive, framed entirely in wood and often surmounted by a wood canopy. They are far more imposing than any made in France at the height of the Gothic period and far more numerous. The finest are lavishly decorated with carved and painted or inlaid armorial designs and other embellishments.

A rather unusual aspect of these tester beds is that the posts at the foot of the bed were not attached to the bed itself. The headboard was often part of the wall paneling but the sides of the bed have been cut loose from the walls. The Elizabethan bed represents, no doubt, a transitional development between the wall-cabinet beds of the Middle Ages and the free-standing beds of later periods. The posts of these sixteenth-century beds had the melon-shaped carvings about midway up the square-footed posts, and were often tapered at the top.

Seating forms were generally the same as those of the Gothic period. But by the late sixteenth century two other chairs had been introduced. The all-oak wainscot chair with turned legs and squared stretchers, rectangular seat, scrolled arms and carved back is one form adapted from existing continental designs. Then there was the smaller armless upholstered chair, with padded and covered seat and back, standing on columnar legs that were joined by squared stretchers. For the most part these were ladies' chairs, designed with low backs and without arms so that the fashionable farthingale or hooped skirt could be accommodated.

Provincial all-wood chairs of that day were like the Yorkshire chair, made with turned legs, squared stretchers and carved backs that had two horizontal panels between the stiles. These Tudor designs derive from the wainscot chairs but are more modest in size and carved decoration.

Upholstered stools and benches were covered in this period with matching fabrics or needlework to create a suite of furniture in a room. These Elizabethan benches, unlike their simple Gothic ancestors with two trestle supports, had a profusion of legs shaped in columns and joined by stretchers. Joined stools with splayed legs in modified melon shapes had carved aprons and rectangular tops. They served as dining chairs and for occasional seating in the great halls of the time.

By the time Queen Elizabeth I assumed the throne in 1558, the trestle table had begun to disappear from the dining halls of the medieval castles. In its place came tables with fixed tops and equipped with leaves to adjust the

Elizabeth I oak refectory table is of draw-leaf design, standing on foliate-urn legs distinguished by gadrooned necks and Ionic capitals, joined by molded stretchers that serve as foot rails. *Parke-Bernet Galleries* (*Taylor and Dull photo*)

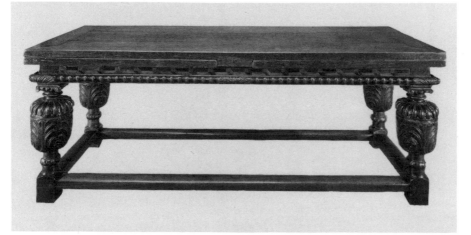

length. This functional aspect made it possible for tables to be used for everyday occasions and to expand for those turbulent feasts so popular after the hunt or during holiday seasons. The precursor of the gateleg table, a design with one pivoting leg to support a fold-out tabletop, is a late sixteenth-century develop-ment. In spite of these innovations, however, the demise of the trestle table did not come in England until well into the seventeenth century, so functional were they for homes where one served for all entertaining.

Cupboards in sixteenth-century England were massive furnishings. The Elizabethan court cupboard stood on short squared legs, was fully enclosed at the base by a pair of paneled doors. When used in a hall or parlor, cupboards were open at the base for the display of tablewares, and this open section was framed by bulbous melon legs.

The tops of all these cupboards were either completely open or had storage cabinets covered by carved doors and set back to create a shelf for the display of additional wares. Often these cupboards bore Renaissance carved details. Gadrooning sprouted on aprons, foliage was carved on cornices and winged griffins appeared on shelf supports. But the silhouettes remained utterly simple and massive in the Gothic mode.

Elizabethan furniture, like Gothic designs, was very much in demand with the turn-of-the-century and later collectors of antiques in this country. Vast collections were dispersed in England prior to 1929 and brought here to fill the mansions of the wealthy. Many of these collections changed hands in the 1930's at deflated prices. But today most are extremely difficult to find in antiques shops and at auctions. Their rarity, however, does not mean that prices are inordinately high. Court cupboards found as recently as five years ago commanded $500 in the shops. Wainscot chairs were $300 to $800. And the chests commanded $400 to $1000. Naturally all these categories command even higher prices—in four and five figures—when the furnishings have known provenance or the workmanship is extraordinary.

chapter 2

RENAISSANCE THROUGH JACOBEAN

ITALY

The Italian Renaissance was an age of magic, a time when awesome artistic genius, intellectual discipline, an abundance of craft skills, affluence and an audience with an insatiable appetite for beauty, combined to reintroduce classicism and humanism to the world.

In the decorative arts the effects were immediate and long lasting. Aroused from the comatose standardization of the Middle Ages, Italian artists and artisans created a style so distinguished and so vital that its effects would be felt for centuries throughout Europe.

As its name implies, the movement began as an intellectual reawakening, a reevaluation of ancient Greek and Roman classical concepts of man and the forms with which he surrounded himself in art and architecture.

From the early fifteenth into the seventeenth century, artists and craftsmen touched everything in their environment with a new beauty. They shaped buildings and furnishings into glorious classical forms. They developed a whole new repertory of craft techniques. Intarsia, *pietra commessa, pastiglia,* certosina and *pietra dura* were skillfully employed to enrich the surfaces of walls, floors, ceilings and furniture. In the fifteenth century furniture came to be regarded as a work of art in itself, attracting the talents of Botticelli and Signorelli, who decorated cassoni and other designs as seriously as if they were executing paintings to be hung on a wall.

Exotic materials that had been abandoned by the Romans in the first centuries after Christ, after hordes of invaders had swept through Europe, were now revived. Silks and velvets, jewels, tooled leathers, semiprecious stones, metals, rare woods, which had been practically unknown in the decorative arts of the Middle Ages, were now brought into wide use to embellish the exteriors and interiors of ducal palaces and merchants' homes.

The furniture of the early Renaissance was wed to its architecture. The square, simple silhouettes of the tables, cassoni (chests with lift-up lids), credenzas (tall cupboards with drawers at the top) mirrored the shapes of the buildings in which they were used. Particularly in Florence, the seat of the Renaissance, furnishings represented an understatement and refinement of form. This characteristic would continue in Florentine furnishings long after such other centers as Venice opted for more baroque silhouettes.

But at the same time, Florentine artisans knew how to embellish their designs with highly sophisticated and ornamental surfaces. Intricate carving and gilding covered structural parts. Heads and busts in high relief formed the stiles. Feet were modeled after dolphins or lion paws. A pair of scrolls became a crest at the center, and knobs replaced the Gothic blunt endings on the top rail of a sgabello chair back.

The Gothic forms, the boxy chests and cupboards, the panel-backed chairs, continued for a while, but were transformed in this period to lighter-looking, highly decorative storage and seating designs. The æsthetic in art had changed. Freed from the spiritual ties that bound the medieval craftsman to a God-centered art form and therefore stifled individual expression, the decorative arts surged forward in all directions. The Renaissance arts thrived not on the beauties of the inner life, but on those of the outer world.

It was logical that the awareness and enthusiasm for the classical cultures would begin in Italy. The Italians lived surrounded by the ruins of their ancient past and, by the early sixteenth century, were digging up other reminders of that earlier civilization.

It was logical also that this movement, which demanded so much individualism, began among a people who are strongly individualistic. By the height of the Renaissance, each Italian town or area had developed its own definite characteristics in the furniture produced.

Even amateur enthusiasts of the Renaissance style will be able to identify a table as Tuscan because of the columnar legs, a chest as Roman because of the heavy classical carving, or a choir stall as Florentine by its fan-shaped trestle supports.

The Italians were also ready for a more luxurious way of life. From the early years of the thirteenth century, aristocrats of Florence and the merchants of Venice had grown ever more affluent, fattening their pocketbooks and filling their groaning boards with the dividends of their thriving trade. By the fourteenth century the Italians had a fuller understanding of comfort than any of their neighbors to the north or west. And, by the fifteenth century, these merchants, aristocrats and princes of the Church were avidly seeking the accouterments of living that would satisfy their yearnings for ease and luxury.

The chairs of the Renaissance period reflect this desire. The *Dantesca,* or Dante chair as some called it, is the easy chair of the Renaissance. This curule X-form chair first appears at the end of the fifteenth century; it is the granddaddy of the modern director's chair. The *Dantesca*'s leather seat and back are slings stretched between the wood sides of the folding frame to cradle the sitter. Even in the twentieth century, when people are accustomed to sinking into mounds of upholstery that cushion every muscle and readjust with every nervous movement, this chair remains one of great comfort. In its day the chair was also extremely practical. It folded, making it easy to transport from room to room or castle to castle.

Although the form and proportions of the chair do not vary in Italy from province to province and decade to decade, the decorative embellishments do. All were used either with exposed leather or with velvet slipcovering the back and the thin seat pillow.

In Venice, for instance, every inch of the curved seat frame is often covered with intarsia, the decorative inlay of light wood against the dark walnut that the Italians used throughout the Renaissance. The stretchers joining the legs at the base are uncarved. In Florence the wood was often left untouched, but the frame is heavier and the stretchers are scalloped at the base or have lion paws for the feet. In Tuscany the arms are fashioned in a downward scroll or end in knobs that are decorated on the sides with carved rosettes.

Thanks to the Renaissance collecting enthusiasms of such twentieth-century tycoons as William Randolph Hearst, the newspaper publisher, Dante chairs are not so rare as one might imagine today. Many of the American millionaires who pillaged Europe from 1890 through the 1920's, with the aid of antiques dealers, were forced to sell their Renaissance and Gothic furnishings during the depression. Others died and their antiques have been dispersed over the years at auctions or through antiques shops at prices far below those at which they were purchased.

The most recent revival of interest in Renaissance furnishings began in the early 1950's. Those who were lucky enough to start buying pieces of the period

Right: Sixteenth-century Florentine Savonarola chair carved in walnut, with a coat of arms centering the back bar, folds for ease in carrying about. Lion's paw feet are carved on the fronts of the base. *French and Company*

Left: carved and partially gilded sgabello chair with double-headed eagle back, octagonal seat and trestle base. *French and Company*

14

then, found bargains at auctions and in all but the most expensive antiques shops. A pair of Dante chairs sold at Parke-Bernet Galleries in 1956 for $35 each. In 1965 three curule armchairs were sold at $150 each. In spite of the jump in price, the chairs were still a bargain at these and higher prices. This indicates that the general escalation in auction prices for antiques has not yet affected the Renaissance so much as other periods. On the other hand, the few curule chairs seen recently in the shops carried price tags of from $700 to $1,500. None of these were chairs with very important provenance, nor were they extraordinary in their workmanship.

Wrought iron and steel curule chairs in the same proportions as the *Dantesca,* but with brass knoblike terminations, were also made in the era. But they are exceedingly rare today and when found in shops cost $1,000 or more.

The so-called Savonarola chair is also a curule design that folds. But it is made entirely of wood, X-shaped staves secured by straight arms, runner feet and a rod under the seat. The seat is of narrow slots and the back is of a wider horizontal bar that is generally carved in the center with an armorial or rosette design.

Like the *Dantesca,* the Savonarola frame is sometimes carved, gilded or inlaid with either lighter woods or mother-of-pearl. The front of the runner feet are also often fashioned into lion paws and the arm terminations into scrolls or knobs. Not so many Savonarolas as *Dantescas* appear to have survived, but since they are far less comfortable, they are also in less demand. Prices range from $100 to four figures.

The straight-backed chair with padded seat and back comes into its own in this period for the first time in history. Made in the sixteenth and seventeenth centuries, these thronelike designs were used for dining, at a desk, or as side chairs. At first they had unpadded leather covering the back and seat. Later the softer, fabric-covered chair appears. Like the curule chairs, these also had trestle supports, adorned with the usual lion paws in front. Many had carved wood brackets or stretchers between the front legs, and squared stretchers on the sides and on the backs.

In time, the legs were sometimes treated to carved or turned decoration. The back stiles were topped with finials that were incised with leaf motifs or fashioned into knobs or animal heads. The same style chair is also found with wood seat or back. Some have backs made up of two horizontal splats that are pierced and carved in leaf and in scroll patterns, with the front stretcher carved to match. Others have flat carving with painted armorial or scenic designs decorating the solid-panel backs. Again the range in price on these chairs is considerable, from $100 to four figures. But they are not uncommon, and good buys can be found.

The sgabello is another typical Renaissance wood chair. It is smaller and most unusual in shape. It has a carved and sometimes pierced back that is shield-shaped and is often carved with the coat of arms of the aristocrat for whom it was made. The seat is octagonal or oval. The base is of two solid carved panels set into the seat at front and at the back. Variations on this form of chair, having three or four plain or baluster-turned legs, also exist. They were made from the fifteenth through the seventeenth century, and range from $75 to $2,000 in price.

Benches and choir stalls were also used for seating in homes and churches in the period and during the revivals of Renaissance furniture that have occurred in this century. At San Simeon, Hearst's California castle, choir stalls were placed against the two long walls of the great dining hall, much to the amusement of the Hollywood movie stars who visited the newspaper publisher there. The choir stalls and single seats range from $150 to four figures. Benches are to be found for $200 up.

A far rarer and eminently useful multiple seating design for those who like their accommodations firm, is the cassapanca. This all-wood bench has a box-like base, a seat that lifts up revealing storage space below, and wood-paneled back and sides. When padded with pillows it frequently serves as an extra sofa in today's home. But prices run higher than for plain benches, from $600 up.

The cassapanca is probably an evolution of the cassone, the lidded chest of the Renaissance that was frequently used for seating. Cassoni were among the most decorated furnishings of the Renaissance period, and it is in the embellishments of those rectangular boxes that one can see the differences between the styles of one province and another. The chests of the fifteenth century made in the Piedmont area are still covered with Gothic tracery. In Tuscany the more "modern" fleurs-de-lis, winged lions, gods, goddesses, sea serpents and foliage cover the front panels.

Sicilian chests are covered with an overall decoration and have mythological birds and animals worked into the design. In Lucca, lions and horses cavort in naturalistic settings painted on these low chests. The differences appear to be endless, as do the techniques employed. Paint, *pastiglia,* carving, gilding, intarsia, polychromed decoration and iron bands cover the front, top and sometimes all of the exposed panels. For the simplest cassoni one may expect to pay $150. But the finest command prices in five figures.

If the artistic finishes on cassoni give clues to where they were made, the credenzas of the Renaissance are the furnishings cited as the most architectural in form and decoration. Credenzas are cupboards with drawers on top and storage behind doors below. They look like miniature buildings with the cupboard doors corresponding to the high-ceilinged, main floor of a palace. The shallow drawers on top are the diminutive match for the low-ceilinged servants' quarters on the upper floor of the fifteenth-century Italian house.

Credenzas range in size from small twenty-inch-long furnishings, called *credenzinas,* to four feet or longer. The church sacristy cupboards that were used to store vestments are also referred to as credenzas, even though the church furnishings often appear without drawers. The façades of credenzas

Early seventeenth-century Tuscan credenza has a drawer hidden in the carved frieze, bronze handles on paneled doors, angels carved on the stiles, and gadrooning on the apron. The walnut design stands on lion's paw feet. *Parke-Bernet Galleries (Taylor and Dull photo)*

echo the entire decorative vocabulary of the period. Grotesques from antiquity are carved into door pulls or entire façades of drawers. Pilasters or sculptured figures of gods and of goddesses frame the doors. Doric, Ionic and Corinthian columns and entablatures appear on the façades of chests. Lion paws, scrolls and foliage form the feet. Acanthus leaves, rosettes, gadrooning, egg-and-dart motifs and armorial patterns center doors and drawers or serve as escutcheons. The most decorative of the credenzas are not always the highest in price, for sometimes simplicity has a higher market value. Prices range from about $400 for small, simple credenzas· to five figures for more important credenzas with proven heritage.

Another comparatively small rare cupboard of the period is the prie-dieu, a furnishing suitable for a person to use when kneeling at prayer. Most are the size of the *credenzina,* having a slant front and a platform built out from the base on which one might kneel in prayer. Demand appears slight for these designs, and prices are from $500 up.

Octagonal-topped tables, a favorite design of the Italian Renaissance style, frequently were supported as here by a tripod base. The scrolled, foliate and paw-carved legs and feet of this walnut design appear below the apron, which is also typically carved with egg-and-dart molding. *French and Company*

Other storage pieces are the chests of drawers that have similar carved decoration and the *bambocci* or writing cabinets with fall fronts, made to stand on bases that were either chests of drawers or credenzas. The *bambocci's* front panel, when open, rests on the chest or cupboard below, and serves as a slanted writing surface. The interior is fitted with tiny drawers and cupboards, as intricately carved as full-sized credenzas. These smaller chests of tiny drawers can still be found, but are becoming quite rare. Very often their prices seem higher than other Renaissance furnishings, ranging from $800 well up into four figures.

Tables proliferated during the Renaissance, multiplying in both size and shape. The structure does not differ greatly from those of the Middle Ages, but the variety shows increased emphasis on specialization. One table no longer had to serve every need in a society of plenty. Three or four or more were used in a single room by members of the aristocracy.

The refectory table, a thick wood top on two or more trestle supports or a columnar base, is certainly the most important. Designed to accommodate from six to twenty persons, refectories range from simple boards on T-shaped trestles, to tops elaborately edged with egg-and-dart motifs or gadrooning set on a variety of fantastically carved supports. Included are the scroll and lion-foot trestles, pairs of twisted dolphins, classical columns, arches and balusters, heroic human figures, and leaf, scroll and columnar combinations. Prices for tables run higher than on other furnishings of this period, ranging from $400 to up to five figures.

The round and octagonal-topped tables run the same stylistic gamut. They have one of three types of bases. The most common is the four-leg base on which the legs splay out at right angles from each other. The most popular shaping is the scroll top with lion-paw terminations. Another base is a fat pedestal, and a third is composed of four legs joined by one continuous stretcher at the base. These medium-sized tables are also very much in demand and would cover the same price range as refectories. Collectors, however, must be wary of very small tables, for few, if any, were made in this period. Most of those said to be Renaissance that measure twenty inches in diameter or in length are generally fabrications of a later date.

SPAIN

Although the Renaissance is treated here country by country, most collectors prefer to mix examples of Italian, Spanish, French, and English and German Renaissance together. The Spanish and Italian designs are the most common mixture and have enjoyed greater public favor in recent years with the current revival of interest in the entire period than have the French, German and later English examples.

In Spain the silhouettes of furniture design are like the Italians, boxy and architectural. But the decoration is quite distinctive and immediately recognizable as Spanish and not Italian. The long occupation of Spain by the Moors, from the eighth century until their defeat in 1492 and final expulsion in 1607, left its mark on furniture. There is a strong taste for geometric design noticeable in furniture, as well as on walls, floors and ceilings. The Moors were Moslems, and the teachings of the Koran made them avoid figural decoration in art.

This did not keep the Spaniards from expressing an exuberant style in the decoration of their palaces and furnishings. Actually the Mudejar style, as the combination of Moorish and Christian elements in art is called, is highly decorative and reaches a level of lushness equal to any other of the time. The sixteenth and seventeenth centuries, when the style flourished, are the greatest period of expansion for these Mediterranean people in their entire history.

Spanish chairs were high and straight-backed, had horizontal leather strips to support the back, and unpadded leather seats. These chairs tend to be far simpler than their Italian cousins. They have understated scroll or curved arm terminations, and geometric carvings on the stretchers joining the front legs.

There were also solid wood chairs, sometimes with arched panels between the

Decorative S-scroll, iron bracing joins the ring-turned baluster legs on this seventeenth-century Spanish table. The carved walnut design has a distinctive heavy plank top extending beyond the carved frieze. The three drawers are separated and framed by foliate corbels. *Parke-Bernet Galleries*

back stiles that ended in turned columns. Top rails were often carved in geometric motifs. Occasionally both styles of chair of this period can be found for as little as $75, but more often than not they command $200 or more in price.

The Spanish tables have two distinctive hallmarks making them unlike most Italian tables of the period. They have heavily carved and splayed, trestle or lyre-shaped supports joined by a decorative iron bracing. Such ironwork occasionally appears on tables made in Italy, but the characteristic is more common to Spain. Any decorative panels on the drawers of such Spanish tables will be geometric rather than classical or figural. Tables in small sizes, about thirty inches long, range from about $300 up, but dining tables measuring from six to ten feet long and thirty inches wide will be from about $800 up.

Ten years ago, when the first mid twentieth-century copies and interpretations of Spanish Renaissance furnishings were imported to this country, most observers felt that the style would never take hold because of its large scale and its weighty, ornate appearance. Nothing could have been further from the truth. The first imports sold in the thousands, and before long most of the Southern furniture producers of this country were adapting Spanish designs into bigger, bulkier furnishings than this country had seen since the 1920's. Although dubbed Mediterranean, the style is rooted not in many lands, but in one—Spain of the seventeenth century.

A design that has not been copied widely in our time but was extremely popular in its day is the vargueno, a fall-front writing cabinet set on top of a chest (*taquillón*) or table (*puente*). The most commonly found examples today are those with façades decorated with wrought-iron plaques in diamond, hexagonal or other geometric motifs, with the metalwork backed by red velvet.

The ornate strapwork, the beautifully worked iron locks and pulls, as well as carrying handles on the side, add to the decorative and virile character of

Geometric motifs decorate many of the extant varguenos of sixteenth-century Spain. This fall-front writing cabinet—fitted inside with a nest of drawers and cupboards richly embellished with carved diamond, circle and star patterns, and inlaid with ivory—is typically faced with wrought iron plaques that are backed with red velvet. The taquillon base is a seventeenth-century chest showing variations of the earlier style. The grotesque masks pull out to support the vargueno's façade when in use. *Parke-Bernet Galleries*

these chests. The interior is richly decorated with mosaics of ivory inlay and polychrome and is as architectural in concept as the Italian *bambocci*. But the Levantine designs of stars, rosettes, quatrefoils, diamonds and hexagons are in sharp contrast to the naturalistic and classical motifs of Italy.

Variations exist showing influences other than the Moorish one. A sixteenth-century Catalan or northern Spanish vargueno, for instance, has a plain undecorated façade, and interior drawers decorated with faces. One of this type, found with its original table base, cost its present owners $350 ten years ago. Today the same design would command $900 or more in a shop. Without a base, such desks bring $400 and up. The Moorish type commands the same prices.

Spain also produced French- and Italian-looking furnishings using linenfold and classical motifs. But these are neither so handsome nor so prized as the Mudejar or Catalan furnishings. One Moorish echo typical in Spain and not found elsewhere is trunklike chests set on low stands. Actually such chests in Moorish Spain sat on the floor in accordance with Arabic culture. With Christianity's return to power, the same chests were raised on trestle supports.

Beds emulated the twisted posts of the Italian baroque, but the headboards are quite distinctive. Arched rows of spindles and a top rail of pierced foliage were two repetitive elements. Tall cabinets, used for the storage of vestments in the sacristies of churches, look like French bread cabinets. They have top sections with spool-turned, ventilated doors, and enclosed lower sections.

FRANCE

In the beginning of the Renaissance, the French, unlike the Spaniards, borrowed fewer of the forms and more of the decorative surfaces from the Italian style. But later even the forms were widely adapted. The Gothic tradition holds in molding silhouettes of cabinets, chairs, tables and chests, but the carver's hand is Italianate and in many cases was probably pure Italian. For it was the custom at the French court to import artists from Italy so that the royal house would reflect the latest fashions.

There are two types of all-wood chairs produced by the French in this era that differ from those made elsewhere. One, made in the reign of Francis I (1515–47), has a lower back than Gothic chairs but the same solid construction. The back of the chair is shaped like a medallion and carved with the profile or full face of a man or woman. The legs are columnar in shape.

The second appeared after Henry II (1547–59) assumed the throne. Called a *caquetoire,* which literally translated means a "chair for cackling," it has a high and narrow back carved with flat moldings, a hexagonal seat and columnar legs. The name derives from the fact that the chair was a favorite among gossiping ladies of the court. Some examples of this design can still be found at about $500 and up. However, since many copies were made in the late nineteenth century, a careful inspection of the construction, wood and finish should be made to determine if the chair is period or not. Most of the reproductions have acquired signs of age and are easily confused with the originals.

The same may be said of the double-decker cupboard, called the *armoire à deux corps.* This design, revived in late nineteenth-century America, has a wide, deep chest at the base and a smaller chest, surmounted by a pediment on top. The form is of course derived from the Italian *bambocci* on a chest, but the French designs are larger in scale and have finer carving. Indeed most of the surface is covered with relief carving of classical motifs and human forms and is often inlaid with marble plaques.

This French chest-on-chest is far less virile and impressive, and therefore less admired by collectors of early furnishings, than either the French Gothic or the Italian Renaissance cabinets. Prices for the originals start at about $800.

Other characteristics of the Renaissance began to emerge in France under the Bourbon monarchs Henry IV (1589–1610) and Louis XIII (1610–43). Although the influences of Italian ornament continued, Flemish motifs also appear in French craftsmanship. The French tread water artistically throughout this period, producing little that is more than derivative in their furnishings. This pause in the development of the French decorative art is certainly partly due to the debilitating effects of the religious wars between the Catholics and the Huguenots that raged between 1562 and 1598.

The first signs of change in attitude toward the arts came in 1608, when Henry IV established free apartments and workshops for artists and artisans. The arts, given this new foundation on which to build, did not come to a full flowering until Louis XIV assumed the throne in 1661, but a start had been made.

The Louis XIII style is today frequently spoken of in fashionable circles, both here and abroad, as a distinctive period of design, and has come to be very much in demand. It is the chairs designed in the era, and the provincial designs, that differ somewhat from those produced in neighboring lands.

The high-backed, richly upholstered chairs stand on either turned legs or lyre-shaped trestles. Arms are curved, terminating in scrolls. Those with X-shaped trestles, often referred to as Louis XIII, rightfully belong to the Louis XIV period. The provincial all-wood chairs with the open backs and turned legs joined by stretchers are one of the choicest designs of the period. Today these small-scaled chairs are used in rooms housing medieval collections at New York's Metropolitan Museum of Art and the Cloisters. Until recently all of these chairs could be found for about $100. Today they command far more, probably two or three times that price. At Parke-Bernet late in 1968, an old but not period version of a Louis XIII chair sold for $325 and was considered a bargain.

The French provincial furnishings of this and later periods are not truly rustic. They were made by local artisans but for châteaus, not peasant homes. In many cases they are now considered more fashionable than the formal furnishings found in Parisian dwellings.

There is a special charm about the tall cupboards with the simple moldings on the doors, and the tables with thick, slab tops and columnar or baluster legs. The trestle tables that remained in use through the mid-sixteenth century and the utterly simple credenzas look as solid and enduring as the French peasant himself. All of these provincial designs are of walnut and oak and are sometimes mistaken for Italian designs of the same period or earlier because of their straightforward simplicity. Most are hard to find in the shops, and the occasional finds command substantially higher prices than Italian designs of the same period. Trestle tables are four figures and up. Smaller tables range from $500, chairs from $200, and small chests from $600 up.

Right: High-backed walnut arm-chairs with down-curving arms terminating in scroll handrests are typical of the Louis XIII style. The square seat and back are covered in the needlework favored in the period. The lyre-shaped legs are joined by a center stretcher and two side stretchers carved to imitate the scrolled arms and curved arm stumps. *Parke-Bernet Galleries*

Below: Strong, simple silhouettes are characteristic of the Louis XIII style. This library table, topped with a thick, rectangular parquetry top, is supported on square legs ending in bun feet and interspaced with turned balusters. The molded stretchers on this walnut design echo both the angular and the curvilinear lines of the supports. *Parke-Bernet Galleries*

ENGLAND

The Renaissance came exceedingly late to England. Although many of such characteristic embellishments of Italian Renaissance furnishings as gadrooning and foliage appeared in the Elizabethan era, it was not until James I ascended the throne in 1603 that pure classical design came to the island kingdom.

The period is called Jacobean, from the Latin *Jacobus* meaning James. Inigo Jones, surveyor general to the king, was the major force in the classical movement. His Palladian architecture and theatrical productions showed the style. But the full force of classicism was never felt in furniture. Throughout James's reign, which ended in 1625, and that of his son Charles (1625–49), very few changes occurred in furniture. The Elizabethan, heavy oak designs continued to reign supreme in most households until Charles II and the Restoration of the monarchy in 1660.

The increased use of upholstery is a significant development of the early Jacobean period. Chairs and settees were made in great numbers for the homes of the wealthy. The settee, a padded version of the all-wood settle, often came equipped with wings, a precursor of the eighteenth-century wing chairs and settees. It also had several legs to give the frame full support. But in spite of the slight changes in chair design, English cabinetmakers or joiners continued to produce oak joint stools, which today cost $300 and up. These stools, used then and today for seating and as small tables, are in great demand because of their double function.

Throughout the Jacobean period, joiners dug deeper into the repertory of Renaissance ornament. Low-relief carving, turned legs and strapwork become commonplace. The gateleg table is an innovation under James I, but even here there is an Elizabethan influence. The table produced in the late sixteenth century, with a single-pivot leg and supporting a folding top, is the ancestor of a Jacobean oak table that had half-round drop leaves on either side of a rectangular top, turned legs and pear-shaped feet. One of this type sold recently for $250.

Austerity marked the short period between the reigns of Charles I and Charles II. Puritanical thinking and the political situation under Oliver Cromwell (1653–58) were immediately reflected in the solid, unpretentious furniture made during the period. Combination designs such as the chair-tables and the chair-settees were high in favor. It is these designs that the Puritans took with them, or remembered, when they left for America. The American colonists' homes were filled with these functional, ultrasimple furnishings.

The Cromwellian chair is certainly one of the most typical designs of the short era. The oak frame, leather seat and back, and knobbed legs have their roots in the Renaissance chairs, of course, but the chair is far less comfortable. The sitter must remain more or less rigid, lest the knobbed parts dig into the

Above: Boldly carved oak cradle and chair are English seventeenth century. Both have
the stylized floral carvings,
finials and darkened finish
favored in the period. The
carved back on the wood-seated
chair is the same style of carving seen in the more imposing
Wainscot chairs produced in
both England and America.
Gertrude Weber

Right: Gateleg table, an innovation under James I, frequently had baluster legs as
here, but rarely was a tilt-top
design. This oak design is
made with wide planks for
the top. *Gertrude Weber*

English oak court cupboard, dated 1665 over the middle upper door, bears the typical flat carving of medallions and floral motifs, is hooded and has two cupboards in the base. *Gertrude Weber*

shins. What could be more appropriate to the thinking of that time, one might well ask.

Occasionally the period produced more decorative designs, as in cupboards that are inlaid with ivory or bone, with or without mother-of-pearl. These storage pieces retain the massive feeling of Elizabethan cupboards, sometimes combining such elements as large bun supports and medallion motifs centering the door panels. They also heralded the changes that would come under the Restoration. The same decorative themes rendered in far more graceful a manner would transform English furniture into baroque design.

chapter 3

BAROQUE THROUGH
WILLIAM AND MARY

◆§ The baroque style, born in Italy in the late sixteenth century, brought to full bloom in France at the end of the seventeenth century, and buried in England and America in the eighteenth century, was a natural evolution from the Italian Renaissance.

"Baroque," a French word from the Portuguese *barrôco,* meaning "a misshapen pearl," is a term not used in the period in Italy; it was applied later by French critics to the irregular forms that were characterized by exuberance and dynamic tension. These critics objected to the abandonment of the classical elements and the ideals of the Renaissance.

Although Rome, often called the baroque city, is the seat of the baroque decorative arts movement, it is in Venice that one finds the finest Italian development of the curvilinear style in furniture. This is the period in which the Counter-Reformation shaped the taste of the public for a sensuous, voluptuous art form intended to excite, not the mind, but the eye and the emotions. The Roman Catholic Church dictated this worldly art form, expressing its power in the lavishly decorated interiors of the churches replete with richly encrusted surfaces showing the carvers', gilders' and artisans' skills.

The sixteenth century had already witnessed increased use of the plastic forms that had been part of the Renaissance style from the beginning. Now the carvers added movement, swirling curves, twisted turns, elaborate drapery treatments, and contorted human forms to the surfaces of furnishings.

It was inevitable that the Italians, once caught up in the spirit of the baroque, would begin to pay more attention to the embellishments of their furnishings than to the woods employed and the cabinetmaking techniques that had for so long made their designs dominant throughout Europe.

The baroque period is characterized by the deterioration in the quality of the woods and forms in the furniture produced. The elaborate carvings and painted surfaces that emerged in the seventeenth century covered the inadequacies of the cabinetmakers' skills. In Venice the style runs wild with whirling forms. Caryatids, used as the stiles of a cassone, swell outward and inward, ending in lion feet.

Foliated and other decorative scroll motifs abound. Shells, cartouches, animal figures of all kinds form thick crusts of ornament, covering the once simple silhouettes of cassoni, the tall credenzas, tables and chairs. As the period evolved, cassoni were all but abandoned in Italy in favor of more specialized furniture forms.

If Renaissance furniture was bold and imposing, baroque furniture is often weighty and disturbingly busy. At its best it represents great rhythmical control and the heights that fantasy can reach. The combination of angelic figures, of caryatids, trophies and foliage at the base of console tables, for instance, has sweeping movement and great charm.

What the Italians lost control of in executing the style that was nurtured in their midst, the French grasped and held with assurance, making it a superior style. By the end of the seventeenth century, the baroque style, as cultivated under the restraining influence of Louis XIV and his cabinetmakers, was being copied throughout Europe, including Italy.

Italian baroque furniture has always been difficult to find in American shops. A few specialists handling the period operate in large cities. But in today's French-dominated antiques market the Italian baroque style has little appeal. Prices are next to impossible to gauge in these circumstances.

LOUIS XIV

The sumptuous baroque style that evolved in France from the mid to late seventeenth century is synonymous with Louis XIV and his reign. For this reason the style is most often referred to as Louis XIV. After Louis XIV became the heir to the throne of France at the age of five in 1643, it was

Anne of Austria, his mother, and Cardinal Mazarin who ruled the country. The Italian-born prelate was responsible for the Italianate character of furnishings that were produced in France by both native and foreign artisans until his death in 1661.

After Mazarin's death, Louis XIV took power and was fully responsible for the arts and furnishings in the ensuing decades. The baroque style was soon devoid of foreign influences and showed complete mastery of forms and decorative embellishments. The king who is supposed to have said *"L'état c'est moi"* (I am the state) might just have well have said *"L'art c'est moi."*

Under such master artists as Charles Le Brun, art director of the realm, the splendor, solemnity and majesty that mirrored the Sun King's view of himself was soon reflected in the decorative arts. Louis XIV considered himself superior to all, a god not a king among men, and worthy of the finest luxuries that could be devised. He had his palaces—Versailles, Trianon, Saint-Germain, Fontainebleau, Marly, Saint-Cloud—lavishly furnished with the products of the workshops that operated under the patronage of the crown.

It was the king's style of living and of entertaining that dictated the turn baroque took in France. Versailles, built as a hunting lodge by Louis XIII, was transformed, beginning in 1668, into a miniature empire where ten thousand persons could be accommodated. The public rooms of the palace were huge, designed for great court assemblages where ceremonies marked by pomp and finery took place. Consequently everything used in decoration and furnishings was on a grand scale producing heaviness in both the proportions and structure of furniture. Rectangular forms, softened sometimes by compass curves, were characteristic. Furniture legs were heavy, square and tapered, joined by diagonal type stretchers. Carved surfaces, although not so elaborate as on Italian furniture, were popular. And gilded finishes appeared on many designs.

The new developments in surface decoration, for which André Charles Boulle, *maître-ébéniste,* was responsible, appear in this period. Chased and gilded bronze appliqués, called ormolu, were used on furniture for the first time, to reinforce and protect the structure and to enrich its appearance. Also new was "boulle work," ebony inlaid with precious woods or marquetry-like inlays in tortoiseshell or gilded brass, of silver or pewter. These decorative techniques continue beyond the baroque period, but ormolu work has had a longer vogue. Indeed, some skilled cabinetmakers still attempt to reproduce ormolu mounts today, especially on reproductions of the period designs.

Boulle's work, like that of most of the renowned artisans who accepted the patronage of Louis XIV, is actually an interpretation in art of the king's stately and imposing ideals. These, plus the ever present nostalgic references to classical antiquity, epitomized Le Brun's vision of the decorative arts. It was Le Brun's conception of the grandeur of the king that molded both the style and the work of the craftsmen employed to execute it.

Louis XIV commode lavishly decorated with marquetry à la Hollandaise, Boulle pilaster at the back and front and ormolu rimming the top, surmounting the pilasters, covering the feet. The pilasters appear to have been added in the early eighteenth century. *Parke-Bernet Galleries*

The French, who had so long made furnishings almost exclusively in walnut and oak, opted for a greater variety. Ebony, oak, walnut, chestnut and sycamore are among the most favored woods of the period. A widespread use of marble for tabletops, and more padding on the stately, high-backed chairs and sofas are two other characteristics of the period.

Although silver furniture was the most luxurious of all made in the Louis XIV period, most of what was made did not survive. National bankruptcy threatened after a series of wars in the seventeenth century. So it was necessary to melt the furniture down to avert financial disaster. Heavy silver mirrors were also banned from manufacture and sale when the national treasury was empty. Fortunately other examples of the period do survive, though most of the finest have long since been deposited in museums.

The high-backed armchairs were lofty enough to protect the powdered periwigs of the aristocrats who reclined in them and wide enough to accommodate the voluminous gowns worn by women of fashion. The chairs had down-curving arms, ending in volute terminations. The legs were pedestal, baluster or scrolled with X- or H-formed stretchers. The finest examples were carved and gilded, but the lesser wood chairs with rounded and modestly carved parts were made for the lesser princes, aristocrats and merchants. These, as well as

Louis XIV armchair with downscrolling arms, squared and columnar legs and high back has an ornately carved frame gilded to suit the opulent aristocratic taste cultivated in the Sun King's reign. *French and Company*

versions made outside France, such as the high-backed designs sold recently at Parke-Bernet, may cost as little as $440 the pair.

Other seating innovations introduced in the Louis XIV period include the bergère, an upholstered wing chair with solid sides; the canapé, a sofa also equipped with wing sides; the banquette, an upholstered bench; and the taboret, an upholstered stool. This is also the period when suites of furniture appear for the first time. Matching chairs and sofas were destined to remain a part of the sitting room, then called a drawing room, down to our time.

Smaller chairs and seating designs became even more widely favored in this period. The *chaffeuse*, a small and upholstered armless chair with short legs and a high, narrow back, was easy to move about in rooms and low enough to perch on before the fire. The *carreaux,* flat cushions on the floor, augmented the framed seating designs, which were never available in sufficient quantity. And the small, wood-frame chair with straw seat and turned legs that the French called *chaise à capucine,* continued to be used.

There were also the folding stools called *pliants,* and backless and armless chairs known as *perroquets,* that were generally used for dining. In this age before separate dining rooms became commonplace in a home, these folding chairs were eminently practical because they could be packed away or moved to other parts of the room so easily after the table was cleared. Although rare, occasionally stools are found for $400.

Consoles come into their own in the late seventeenth century, and were treated as an integral part of the design of a room. These tables were placed against a wall under a trumeau, the mirror with decorative details across the top, and the console and trumeau became one design element.

Consoles had carved aprons or friezes and stood on legs fashioned in scroll or pedestal shapes. The variety of bases and types of stretchers joining the legs is impressive. But the form more often than not is lost under excessive carving. Slightly less ornate are the plain or painted tables. But other specialized tables, for writing, games, dressing, coffee or to hold a candlestick, continued to develop, lavished with every form of decoration known to cabinetmakers of the time.

The *bureau plat,* a flat-topped writing table with drawers in the frieze, was a favorite of Boulle's. It frequently was provided with a separate unit with open sections or drawers for storing papers or writing equipment, called a *serre-papiers.* It was placed at the back or at one end of the table. Later the *serre-papiers* acquired its own stand or chest and stood next to and at the same height as the table.

Another desk of the period was the *bureau à gradin,* a table surmounted by a long unit of pigeonholes and drawers placed at the back of the writing table. There was also the *bureau semanier,* a unit of two tiers of drawers standing on scroll or baluster legs at either side of a kneehole.

All these desks were richly decorated with ormolu, carved and gilt wood, ebony veneers or a marquetry of tortoiseshell and metal. Equally decorative, although far lighter and smaller, were the two-tier *cabaret à café* tables that were used for serving coffee or chocolate.

The Louis XIV period still commands escalated prices, but not at the high level of many eighteenth-century designs. A Louis XIV writing table, for example, can still be found from $1,000.

The commode is a logical evolution of the console, a development that occurred around 1690. The French had an ever increasing need for storage tables. So the console was filled in at the base with two or three drawers and placed under the trumeau in the same way as the console had been.

One strange element is the use of eight legs to support some of these early commodes. But Boulle managed to avoid the eight legs, substituting curved braces that ended in gilt corkscrews for four of the legs. A recent ormolu-encrusted commode of this type, a rare example of Boulle's work, brought $50,000 at an auction.

Other notable storage pieces of the period were the armoires and the bookcases. Boulle has been credited with devising the first bookcases around 1700.

These were not large, standing no more than four feet high and six feet long. Doors, decorated either with wood-framed interlaced wire or merely backed by shirred curtains, hid the contents from view.

Beds were choice furnishings used less for sleeping than for semi-reclining at small dinners. Beds were a sign of wealth and were placed prominently in small salons in a home where special guests were entertained. Only on rare occasions were these richly draped beds used by French nobles or even their illustrious guests for sleeping.

THE LOW COUNTRIES

Elsewhere on the Continent the baroque style took different forms and affected other furnishings. In Flanders the caned seat and back was introduced on armchairs by the mid seventeenth century. These chairs retained the basic form of the Renaissance. The turned stiles, pierced top rail and front stretcher and the curved arm ending in volute are all retained from that earlier epoch. In the same period, ebony-veneered cabinets lavishly painted in the manner of Rubens with classical and mythological motifs, carved or decorated with inlaid wood and marble, came into use.

In 1685 or thereafter, Daniel Marot, the French architect, and many of his colleagues and fellow countrymen, sought refuge in Holland following the revocation of the Edict of Nantes that marked the renewal of the religious troubles for Protestants in France. Unlike Flanders, where the Counter-Reformation bound the people closer to the French style and tastes, the Dutch Protestants developed a native style that was markedly different from that of their neighbors to the south.

It was Holland that served as the major influence on England in the late seventeenth and early eighteenth centuries. From the Restoration through the William and Mary period, a parallel development can be seen in Dutch and English decorative arts. But the English showed greater restraint than the Dutch in their carving and in the degree of elaboration in decoration.

This influence began to decline at the beginning of the eighteenth century. But vestiges will linger as long as walnut remains the English cabinetmakers' wood. Walnut, admired in England since the sixteenth century because of its use in continental furniture, began to be cultivated in the island kingdom, but was not in great supply there until the mid seventeenth century.

The peak period in Dutch furniture lasted from 1660 to 1690. During this time Oriental influences and chinoiserie became widespread in Holland, because of the Dutch East India Company's increased trade with the East. Cabinets were created for the display of exotic tablewares, jade curios and other imports from the East. Tea tables came into being. And the carved and painted fantasies blending Dutch and Chinese motifs freely in both figural ornaments and scenic designs, marked many furnishings.

It is from Holland that the English took the form that would become the Queen Anne chair. But the Dutch did not originate this design. Its ancestor, no doubt, is the Chinese Ming chair. The cabriole leg ending in a cloven hoof, the curved chair back, the pierced splat shaped to the sitter's back—elements that herald the coming of the Queen Anne chair—appeared in Holland in the last decades of the seventeenth century. This prototype is far lighter, more shapely and imaginative than the earlier Marotesque chair, which had heavy, ornately carved straight legs, a pierced solid wood back and ornate stretchers.

The skills of Dutch marquetry artisans are best seen in the cabinets—those tall, square designs that are like a chest-on-chest. Floral motifs cover every surface in refined inlays that were frequently polychromed. Later the Dutch settlers in America would modify the designs. The *kas* or *kast,* as the tall cupboard with two doors is called, also was decorated with marquetry or carved with geometric forms.

ENGLAND

The English never fully embraced the baroque style, although influences from the Dutch baroque were apparent in both the forms and decoration of English furniture through the reigns of Charles II (1660–85), James II (1685–88), William and Mary (1689–1702) and, to a lesser degree, through to the end of the age of walnut in the eighteenth century.

One reason for the English resistance to the baroque style is that the island kingdom was, in many ways, still steeped in the Middle Ages. The exuberance of the baroque was foreign and unnatural. England needed the transition period of the Renaissance to nurture the style. And the Renaissance had all but bypassed England as it galloped through Europe in the sixteenth century.

In Roman Catholic countries where the style flourished, the Counter-Reformation movements had sparked, indeed encouraged, the art movement. Architects and artists lavished the glories of its sensuousness and naturalism on the walls and ceilings of churches, shaping architecture and sculpture to the restless, vigorous style. But Protestant nations never felt comfortable under the mantle of baroque art. Thus the twists and turns, the exaggerated swelling and undulations that were characteristic of late seventeenth-century art elsewhere, never took root in England. Nor did the element of fantasy, suggested first in Venetian furniture and so fully developed in France under Louis XIV.

What did happen after Dutch craftsmen emigrated to England and the country began to experience new influence was that many of the techniques of baroque were wed to traditional forms. Jacobean chairs sprouted caned seats and backs. Lacquered cabinets appeared and were embellished with marquetry worked in floral patterns. Inlays of other precious materials and gilding testified to the enriched spirit. The scroll, one of the strongest characteristics of the baroque style, was soon evident in furniture supports.

One of the most notable achievements in England during this era of restrained exuberance is the development of veneering techniques. Parquetry was very much in favor, executed with inlays of ivory and wood or in a technique called oystering. The latter uses circles or ovals called oyster shells of wood cut against the grain from branches. It was employed on tables and other surfaces.

Marquetry in contrasting woods, stained or sometimes polychromed, appears for the first time in England. The floral and bird designs that the Dutch had fashioned with such brilliance, are adapted to the English taste.

The brilliantly colorful marquetry of the Caroline (Charles II) period was replaced under William III by a more subdued form of marquetry embellishment that looks like rambling foliage and is called seaweed or arabesque marquetry. The lacy, filigree patterning that covered chests, secretaries, tables and tall-case clocks required the greatest skill, as did the inlaying of metal, to heighten the marquetry effect.

It was under Charles II that the Oriental influence reached its peak. The taste for Chinese goods had long been cultivated ever since trade and exploration first brought the Orient to England's doorstep in the time of Elizabeth I in the late sixteenth century. But not until the baroque style insinuated itself into English culture, did such practices as lacquering or japanning commence in cabinetmakers' workshops.

In 1688, just before William and Mary became joint sovereigns of England, a technical paper on the subject called *A Treatise of Japanning and Varnishing* was written by John Stalker and George Parker; after its publication, the paint floodgates were opened. Sometime afterward such red japanned chinoiserie designs as the slant-front bureau-cabinet that sold in London in 1968 for $21,000 were made in reasonably large quantity.

The skills of the upholsterer, the parcel-gilders, the gesso and silver workers can be seen in other furnishings. In wood carving the superior talents of Grinling Gibbons (1648–1721) came to the fore. The pierced foliage in swirling patterns that characterized his style was often imitated but never matched.

In furniture the changes that the baroque brought can be seen most in the marked differences in chair design. Cane, introduced from the Orient via Holland, was first used on chairs with turned legs, arms, stretchers and stiles. Later the more graceful Charles II chair, with high back, curved arms, pierced and carved front stretcher and scrolled leg, appears. A set of six caned seat designs with oval caned back panels framed by twisted uprights, in a barley sugar pattern sold recently for $950.

Under Charles, who was sympathetic with his cousin Louis XIV, luxuries of the French court were introduced in England. Upholstered chairs began to show the Gallic fashion when they appeared dripping with fringes and tassels. High-backed chairs, sometimes with legs ending in outward volute-feet, also in the Louis XIV manner, came into use, as did wing chairs that were then called "easie" chairs. And to match the wing chair there was the upholstered daybed and settee. Possibly also in imitation of his French relative, Charles became a patron of the arts, supporting the Mortlake tapestry workshop and several other areas of the decorative arts.

The Caroline period brings the introduction of dining rooms and the newer oval and round tables, frequently equipped with gateleg bases. Many of the more affluent homes had several tables in the dining room where large numbers could be accommodated at small or medium-sized tables, rather than the single, banquet-sized trestle tables that had groaned with feasts since the Middle Ages. Dining-room serving tables and a variety of other smaller tables for games and food multiplied. Today even simple examples of such designs can skyrocket to close to $7,000. But crudely made or modest tables from the era can be found, with searching, for from $300 to $800.

Fall-front writing cabinets on stands, like those devised in Renaissance Italy, were introduced in England around 1660. Also in use were portable desks equipped with drawers and a slant front. The late seventeenth century saw the beginning of widespread use of chests of drawers. The high esteem in which they were held can be easily understood after even a cursory examination of the superb marquetry or carved geometric embellishments on their surfaces.

Gateleg table with barley turnings for supports, and on drop leaf supported by the swing-out support, is English seventeenth century. The oak design has an interesting apron under both the table top and the upper stretcher of the swing-out leg. *Gertrude Weber*

In the William and Mary period, Daniel Marot, the French Huguenot, who had sought refuge in Holland earlier, came to England under the sponsorship of his Dutch patron, William III. The elegance and refinement of furniture forms and ornament during the architect's stay, has been attributed to his influence. There was a trend toward simplicity, a trend shown in the wider use of veneers. These were applied to flat surfaces, exposing the finest characteristics of wood grain and crossbanding. Walnut dominates the scene throughout this period.

Certainly the most distinctive hallmark of the William and Mary period is the shape of legs on chairs and tables. Following the Caroline flirtation with turned legs and volute shapes, England settled down on the baluster leg. It was carved in a variety of ways, but almost always it is trumpet-shaped or topped with a cap, and terminates in a globular, squared or underscrolled Spanish foot.

There is a noticeable lightening in shape of chairs. The ramrod-straight backs are slimmed down and stretched to new heights to cradle the flamboyant wigs of the day. The cane seats and backs, as well as the pierced crests on top rails and front stretchers, and the tapering shapely legs, add to the new and airy look.

The cartouche-shaped, pierced-back chair, associated with Marot, was also

William and Mary oak table standing on slender, modified trumpet and ball legs joined by an X-shaped stretcher has a gracefully modeled apron. The chair, by contrast, is bolder, standing on squared legs in back, baluster legs in front. The chair back has five flat spindles topped by a crest rail of scrolls and pierced carving. *Gertrude Weber*

made in England at the end of the seventeenth century. From there to the simpler, splat-back, cabriole-legged design, the same step that the Dutch took a few years earlier, brought the English to the beginnings of what became known as the Queen Anne chair.

China cabinets were new to England, coming rather belatedly across the seas for the Orient via France and Holland. Porcelain wares and Delft faience filled the shelves of these cabinets and became a symbol of affluence in that era. The cabinets were, true to their origin, lacquered or japanned, as the imitative finish was called in England. Many of the finest were placed upon some of the most elaborate stands ever produced in England.

The Welsh dresser, a provincial design that assumed the silhouette of English court cupboards, simplified it and set it on baluster legs, functioned for the middle classes as the china cabinets did for the aristocracy.

The tea table, soon to become the symbol of English life, is another late-century innovation that came into being when tea was still reserved for medicinal use or, as a beverage, could be sipped only by the very wealthy. The tray-

Welsh-type dresser from Derbyshire is an eighteenth-century interpretation in oak of the early court cupboard. This provincial design is hooded, has a scrolled frieze and stands on short stump feet instead of baluster legs. *Parke-Bernet Galleries*

topped tables were circular or oval and had a variety of four-legged and pedestal bases.

The dressing or toilet table that came to be called a lowboy is an outstanding design of the era. Legs have baluster shaping, topped by inverted cups and tapering to the X-form stretcher. Feet are rounded, in teardrop or ball shapes.

The tallboy, or chest-on-chest, also made its debut a bit later. But its fuller development did not come until the Queen Anne period. Even more important, however, is the secretary-cabinet. This double-decker design was embellished in the top section with a pierced frieze and arched moldings above the double-doors and, in the lower section, was fitted with drop-down writing compartment and drawers.

Late seventeenth-century English furnishings represent good buys today, although most designs from the period are becoming exceedingly rare. In the 1920's and thirties, when the ancestral holdings of many British families flooded the antiques market, prices were far higher. Over the last few years relatively few designs from the period have appeared at auction. Most, like the William and Mary side tables sold late in 1968 at $75 and at $250, would be considered extremely modest. Earlier, a William and Mary oak stool brought $190, a chest-on-stand $225, a cabinet-on-stand $600, a tallboy $100 and a candle-stand $200.

What holds true for the Jacobean and Renaissance designs also holds for William and Mary. Modest examples command modest prices, but the fine pieces rise into four figures or more. The William and Mary state bed sold late in 1968 for $2,300 was considered an important example of the period. Made about 1685 for the town house of Sir Dudley North, it was later moved to Glenham Hall, Suffolk. Ostrich plumes crown the corners of the molded cornice. The entire interior—headboard and bed covering—are covered with floral embroidered cream satin, and the testers are hung with crimson velvet. But there is more than upholstery and needlework shown. The gilded feet of the oak corner posts are carved cherubs seated on scrolls and are detachable. Even though mostly of fabric, the bed is a masterly exercise in interpreting baroque as it was known in England.

chapter 4

FRANCE
Régence through Directoire

◆§ Political, economic and cultural control slipped slowly from Louis XIV's grasp during the last twenty-five years of his life and reign. The palace of Versailles, a once-glittering monument to the Sun King's power and glory, appeared tarnished and dull by the beginning of the eighteenth century. So did the classically severe furnishings that had been designed to match the image of the august king.

Under the religious and moral influences of Madame de Maintenon, the king had imposed strict austerity on his court—a move that would cause a sharp reaction in the ensuing decades. If the times mold the man, they certainly mold the furnishings he sits on, eats from, and surrounds himself with. The formal grandeur of the French monarch's court was a thing of the past. The stateliness of the furniture created for that court ceased to be meaningful.

New forms and decoration registering this relaxation of royal standards, brought a softening of line and grace to the decorative arts that was unknown in the seventeenth century.

The Régence period, as are called the years between 1715 and 1723, the span when Philippe II, duc d'Orléans served as regent for Louis XV, is a transitional period. The silhouettes and symmetry of Louis XIV remained, but the ornamentation of the more charming style of Louis XV began to emerge. In the Régence period it is the decorative embellishments that dominate in the fashioning of commodes, fauteuils, and escritoires. Furniture seems washed—indeed almost drowned—in lacy, figural, flat carving, in painted decoration and ormolu appliqués. By the end of the first quarter of the eighteenth century, exotic and lavish surface treatments would begin to blend with new, more appropriate forms, restoring harmony to this branch of the decorative arts.

In spite of this conflict, there is much to admire and respect in Régence furniture. The eye is charmed by the play of chinoiserie, that blending of Oriental and European elements in painted decoration, on the façades of commodes and on the tops of chests. The mind delights in the endless variations of singerie that produce monkeys and apes in fantastic shapings on finials and escutcheons. And excitement stirs on viewing the translation of the

Grotesque masks at the knees, a male mask at the base, and the portrait medallion centering the apron of this fine early Régence console show the influence of the theater in furniture of the first quarter of the eighteenth century. The walnut, wall-hung design has a *rouge royale* marble top. *Parke-Bernet Galleries*

commedia dell'arte to furniture. Harlequin, Columbine and Scaramouche play out their theatrical ventures on drawer fronts and cupboard doors.

The Oriental influence in furniture was due in large part to expanding trade with the Far East in this period. The entire repertory of Chinese imagery— the pagodas, arched bridges, peacock plumage, dragons and monkeys and pearls, are transformed into fantastic painted scenes by such notable artists as Antoine Watteau.

But the translation from the East to the West never occurs without a French accent. What makes these Oriental motifs so lively and amusing is the way they are combined with the traditional Louis XIV vocabulary of ornament. To see a chinoiserie scene framed with acanthus leaves or monkeys clambering up colonnades lends an element of fantasy to furniture.

One of the most proficient craftsman of the period was Charles Cressent. This master of applied ornament was a sculptor who actually made all the models for the bronzes and watched over the completion of these ornaments. It is to Cressent that we owe the appliqués of foliage, masks, scrolls and *espagnolettes* (busts of smiling women) capped on the knees of curved legs or adorning the façades of commodes or forming the pulls on drawers. It is Cressent who cultivated a taste among the French for the darker, exotic woods that contrasted so beautifully with the bronze appliqués or ormolu mounts for which he, more than any other *ébéniste,* was noted.

Clues to the Régence style in chairs can be seen in more than the surface decoration. Lighter silhouettes began to appear around 1715. No longer imposing in the height or weighty appearance, the Régence chair bears a shorter, curved leg that ends in a small scroll or volute. The arms are centered by padded rests. The backs are lower and upholstered with the frame exposed. Gone by the late Régence are the stretchers that joined the heavy legs of Louis XIV chairs. The new slimmer legs are lighter and, to give the necessary support, carved aprons appear between the legs. But the chair retains its squared corners, its rectangular shape. The rounding of the seat, the next step in the evolution of the chair, postdate the Régence and marks the opening of the Louis XV era.

Prices for the Régence chairs are, for the most part, lower than the imposing Louis XIV, the pure rococo of Louis XV, and the neoclassic designs of Louis XVI. Period continental fauteuils of uncertain nationality can still be found at $250, but for a good French chair of this type one must expect to pay $800 and up. A set of twelve Régence gilt-wood, tapestry-covered fauteuils were sold not long ago for $10,000. Even dining-room chairs of the style made after the period run $800 or more for a set of six.

In other areas of Régence furniture the same moderate to high prices are the rule. A pair of small two-doored corner cabinets, called encoignures, were sold at auction for $1,700. Both were dressed with ormolu mounts, had marble tops and were in excellent condition, but lacked a maker's name. At the same recent sale a fine kingwood, bombé commode with a red marble top brought $3,250.

Régence settee supported on carved cabriole legs joined by a boldly carved apron repeating the shell, cabochon and foliage details of the legs. The seat, bowed in front,
square in back, represents a transition between the squarer Louis XIV and more
rounded Louis XV seating designs. *Parke-Bernet Galleries*

LOUIS XV

The fantasizing of cabinetmakers reached new heights in the Louis XV
period. Rococo, the style that evolved from 1720 to 1760, spun decoration to
dizzying heights, reflecting the king's own pursuit of pleasure, luxury and
entertainment.

The caprices of cabinetmakers centered around four basic forms—rocks,
shells, flowers, and foliage—but the variations on these visual themes appear
unlimited. They were used alone or with the other motifs favored in the
period. Floral bouquets, tied or in baskets; palm and laurel leaves; pastoral,
music and agricultural themes; chinoiserie and singerie, also played a part in
shaping the new curvaceous style. And in this profusion of curvilinear carving,
the symmetry, rectilinear forms and straight lines from Louis XIV and Régence
completely disappear.

As with so many terms commonly used to designate periods in art history,
the word "rococo" was never used to identify the Louis XV style during the
era. Rococo derives from the French word *rocaille,* meaning "rockwork." One
form of rockwork seen in the mock grottoes that the French and Italian nobles
had installed in their gardens since the Renaissance times was, by the late
eighteenth century, called *rocaille*. These grottoes were dazzling tributes to the

skills of ornamentists. Natural rocks speckled with shells and glittering pebbles tumbled like waterfalls, were shaped into stalactites and fashioned into lapping waves in these ersatz marine grottoes. Since these were elements that were in time adapted in the Louis XV period, the word *rocaille*—and in the nineteenth century the term "rococo"—became synonymous with the exuberant style.

Rococo is the most feminine of all styles, a natural evolution from seventeenth-century baroque. Ever since Louis XIV surrendered his imperious grip on the empire in 1690, a softening that comes with age had increasingly characterized the king's life and that of the arts of his kingdom. The florid fantasies that erupted during the rococo period glorified not a king, but pretty women everywhere.

Furniture was only one small aspect of the effeminate influence that pervaded all of French life and art. Louis XV's mistress, Madame de Pompadour, who "reigned" from 1745 until her death in 1764, certainly was a major cause for this feminizing of French decorative art. Jean François Oeben, *ébéniste* to the king, filled the pavilions, hermitages and châteaus of Madame de Pompadour with some of his choicest work. And so did the majority of other prominent craftsmen and artists.

In this period of political and social decadence, the aristocracy sought amusement in every form possible. The sensuous and pagan were glorified in canvas, in print, in sculpture and in architecture. No wonder furniture designs of the era possessed such grace and voluptuous appeal!

The French cabinetmakers had the skills to provide the aristocracy with the visual diversions they so eagerly sought. The movement away from rectilinear, classical silhouettes that had begun a century earlier in baroque Italy, now reached a peak in the assymetrical, curvilinear fantasies that the *ébénistes* whipped up in the new, all-rounded forms and in the decoration of furniture.

In both boiserie and in furniture, carved decoration declined. In its place far less expensive but more flexible painted decoration was often used. Vivid colors dominated the palette of the decorative artists, and fully painted furniture became quite common. The sculptor's skills were also in evidence, shaping and applying the glittering metal mounts to furniture. And going one step further, some furnishings and woodwork showed even more serious economies. Printed textiles covered panels as a modest substitute for the painter's skills.

But economy was certainly not the prime aim of most of the ornamentalists of the period. In fact it was to be expected that the riotous play of embellishment would go too far. Many of the late rococo designs—commodes in particular—appear encased in webs of metal mounts. The kingwood, mahogany, ebony and lacquered effects all but disappear under the camouflage of these screens of metalwork.

Rococo is a style that brings serpentine or vertical curves and bombé or horizontal curves together on commodes and chests. The sinuous cabriole leg, although not new in this period, is more typical of Louis XV than of its

Curved, cartouche-shaped back, carved at the cresting with flowers and foliage, padded arm rests with voluted supports, a shaped seat and molded apron distinguish this Louis XV beechwood fauteuil made in the mid eighteenth century. *Parke-Bernet Galleries*

predecessor styles. C- and S-curves, flame ornaments, foliage, flowers and cabochons reign throughout on chairs, tables and commodes. And by the peak years of the king's reign, from 1740 to 1760, the vivacity, the almost uncontrollable play of figural line, subsides. The quieter, more restrained designs of the middle years of the Louis XV period result in even choicer designs.

One of the chief characteristics of the mid eighteenth century is the development of mechanical devices that test the *ébénistes'* skills in devising multipurpose furnishings that functioned as dressing tables for work, reading or writing. In lacquer work the chinoiseries continue with such *ébénistes* as the Martin brothers who achieved consummate perfection in the craft. Lacquered furniture in every shape and for every purpose was produced.

The woods changed somewhat in the mid eighteenth century. Ebony was discarded. But oak, walnut, fruitwoods, palisander (Brazilian rosewood), kingwood, satinwood and more than ninety other woods were used in this period when marquetry reached its zenith. Mahogany was not favored throughout most of this era in France.

The cabinetmakers, such as Lazare-Duvaux, Cressent, Georges Jacob, *ébéniste* to Madame de Pompadour, and the German *marqueteurs* lavished their special

The Louis XV bergère, one of the most comfortable chairs ever devised, is often low-slung as on this mid eighteenth-century example. The shaped top rail carved with scrolls and floral sprays, the padded armrests, wide seat and short, shapely cabriole legs make this an exceptional version. From the collection of Madame Lucienne Fribourg. *Parke-Bernet Galleries (Taylor and Dull photo)*

talents on all tables, desks and cabinets of that day. They played freely with geometric and scenic patterns, floral and foliage motifs and trompe l'oeil. Such painters as François Boucher influenced figural decoration in rooms by the tapestries they designed. The effects would also be felt in upholstery and in many forms that were adapted in marquetry and painted designs on furniture. Notable in popularizing tapestry covers on furniture were François Desportes and Jean Baptiste Oudry, animal painters both.

The most important chair of the period is the bergère, a low, wide, upholstered armchair with solid sides. The chair appeared first at the end of the Régence period, around 1720. The three most common versions of the bergères known are those that derive from the Louis XIV fauteuil but have solid sides, those with prominent ears or wings at the back, and those in a gondola shape.

Bergères remain one of the most popular forms of seating, two and a half centuries after their introduction. They were made in great numbers to satisfy aristocrats and the burgeoning merchant class. Today they are readily found both at auction and in antiques shops. But their prices continue to rise, and most are snatched up quickly, no matter how high the price. At a country estate auction not long ago a collection of château furniture with known provenance included a pair of bergères. The pair were sold for $5,000. Dealers claim that no matter where you go today—to city or country shops or auctions —bergères will have an avid following. But, with luck, bergères can still be found for $550 and up.

Canapés, those small settees made to accommodate either two persons (also called a tête-à-tête) or three, were made in fewer numbers. Although they are not so much in demand in this age of softer sofas, prices range from high to astronomical. The most desirable three-seater canapé is oval in shape with arms formed by a downward continuation of the arched back and the base supported by eight cabriole legs. One of this kind sold recently for $800.

Even signed canapés can occasionally be found at modest prices. Late in 1968 a beechwood mid eighteenth-century sofa signed by I. B. Lerouge (Jean-Baptiste Lerouge, M.E.) was sold at Parke-Bernet for $600. The couch had a caned seat and back, and stood on cabriole legs carved at the knees and toes with acanthus leaves. Even the collection was a known one. The canapé formerly belonged to Elizabeth N. Graham (Elizabeth Arden).

Daybeds, although not easy to find, are also not astronomically high today. The daybed was one of the most characteristic designs of the era. To understand its significance, it is important to realize that women were accustomed to receiving visitors in their private quarters and bedrooms at this time. They entertained guests wearing negligees and invariably the mistress of the household preferred reclining on a daybed to sitting on a chair.

The three most popular daybed forms follow chair designs of that day. The duchesse is a two-part daybed, comprising a gondola-bergère and a low-backed, chaise-like footrest. The winged or confessional-type daybed is sometimes made in one piece and is flat at the foot end. It is this design that most closely resembles the chaise as we know it today. In two or three parts, the foot end has a low, gondola-shaped back. The third type of daybed is the *veilleuse,* a cross between a bergère and a canapé. One side, where the sitter rests, is higher and chairlike. The other end is low and joined to the chair portion by a sloping back.

Daybeds, although not impossible to find, are certainly not in abundance in shops or at auctions. Not too long ago a variation on the duchesse, with an adjustable winged back and an adjustable footboard, was available at $1,000. The frame on this design, visible at the base only, was painted an antique white. The covering was of mauve taffeta.

Tables in the Louis XV period abound. One of the few forms that continue to enjoy popularity from the past without significant change is the trestle table used for dining. Actually it was the custom in France, even among kings and nobles, to dine intimately in salons or boudoirs in the company of a few friends, leaving the grand parade rooms for the rare, formal feasts. Thus there was little need to design new large tables. And when large or small trestle tables were used, they were draped with fabric to the floor. This is still a favorite device among the French, a trick used with great success whenever they wish to conceal an undistinguishable tabletop and its rudimentary or unfashionable base.

It is the smaller special-purpose tables that epitomize the elegance and refinement of mid-century life. The great variety of these modest-sized furnishings reflects the scaled-down rooms and the intimacy that the French aristocracy and the citizenry craved. It is on these designs that the *ébénistes* exercised their skills in decoration and construction. The one feature all share is the supple cabriole leg. In most ways each possesses its own distinctive character and shaping.

Among the most important types of small tables is the *ambulante,* a two-tiered design equipped with carrying handles to carry it about with ease. It was used for serving or other needs. The *serre-bijoux* (jewel box), another miniature design, was made with either a lift-up lid or drop front concealing drawers for storing bibelots. The *table à ouvrage* was a worktable where the ladies of the court did needlework.

The poudreuse, or dressing table, was one of the most sophisticated designs of the era. It had hinged end sections that opened outward and a center section fitted with a lift-up mirror and drawers. On the finest examples, sections were fitted with fine French porcelain bottles and containers for toilet needs. These toilet tables were designed mostly for women, but there were those for men as well. But the price range now is wide, from $700 to $3,000 or more.

Another example of the increased role women played in French society and the way cabinetmakers catered to distaff whims is the ultrafeminine miniature chest called the *bonheur du jour.* It had a small superstructure at the back concealing storage space for writing materials behind doors or in drawers. A Louis XV innovation, this table was most fashionable under Louis XVI. Recently an extremely fine example was sighted with a price tag of $2,100, and a signed version made by P. Roussel with extraordinary marquetry worked into patterns of bridges, buildings, a boat and swans brought $6,000 at auction not long ago.

There were other tables—those for bedside use were called *tables de chevet* and *tables de nuit.* The latter, a short-legged design, often with a drawer at either end, was often handsomely embellished with choice marquetry. And like one such design that was on the market recently for $1,600, such useful designs command better than moderate prices. Those for games, called *tric-tracs* (the French word for backgammon) and *bouillottes,* run easily into four figures and are rarely found for less. Then there are tables for sewing supplies and accessories known as *chiffonières,* and others for reading. Signed tables will, of course, command the highest prices. Therefore, when $4,000 was the price won at auction recently by a signed François Reizell late Louis XV table, no one was surprised. Even a higher price would not have raised eyebrows when this parquetry-covered, three-drawer design with a small shelf at the base between the subtly curved cabriole legs, was presented.

Right: A Louis XV *bon-heur du jour* has tambour doors concealing the back superstructure of drawers surmounting a pedestal equipped with more drawers. The tall, slender cabriole legs end in ormolu leaf sabots on this tulipwood desk signed by Guillaume Cordie. *Parke-Bernet Galleries*

Left: Delight in games and in the furnishings created for them was characteristic of the Louis XVI style. This signed example of a gaming table by Godefroy Dester is mounted in bronze doré and has an ebony backgammon well inlaid in bone. The *acajou* (mahogany) table stands on square tapering legs and castered feet. *Parke-Bernet Galleries*

50

Left: A kidney-shaped table, its top banded with ormolu and inlaid with a musical trophy, its sides lavishly decorated with marquetry, is typical of the work on the variety of small tables of the Louis XV period. A small slide pulls out from below the top and above the door on this kingwood and rosewood table signed by G. Péridiez. *Parke-Bernet Galleries*

Right: Chevron stripes of tulipwood within rosewood borders cover the façade and top of this three-drawer table. The slender, shaped legs end in ormolu sabots matching the ormolu escutcheons. *Parke-Bernet Galleries*

Specialty tables such as this short-legged *table à lit* superbly worked in parquetry of rosewood and kingwood have side drawers and a center drawer fitted for writing materials. *Parke-Bernet Galleries*

A maroon-leather topped *bureau plat* in tulipwood of the Louis XV era relies for its decorative appeal on the curvilinear shaping of the silhouette and on the ormolu mounts rimming the top and dressing up the drawer fronts and legs. This desk is a signed example of the work of Jean Baptiste Tuart and dates from the mid eighteenth century. *Parke-Bernet Galleries*

Writing tables enjoy the same popularity. The *bureau plat,* a writing table that usually came equipped with a raised section for storing papers called the *serre-papiers,* that was placed at the rear or side of the table, continues in favor. But full-scale desks, called *bureaus à cylindre,* became the triumph of the *ébénistes'* skill from the mid eighteenth century onward. Jean François Oeben has been credited with the creation of this design, with its curved façade that covered the writing section and concealed the pigeonholes and drawers that were so skillfully fitted inside. A choice example signed by Jacques Dubois recently brought $3,250.

Still another writing desk was the fall-front *secrétaire à abattant*. Above the fall front, the bureau was equipped with a drawer. The base had two drawers or two doors behind which there were shelves for storage. During a recent sale a Louis XV formal design and one of provincial origin sold for $1,500 and $900 respectively. Obviously there is a telling difference between the two, a fact shoppers become readily aware of at auctions and in antiques shops. Provincial designs of other writing designs, such as the kneehole desk and tall *secrétaires* may be compared in the same manner.

Right: The *bureau à cylindre*, on which *ébénistes* lavished their skills in parquetry and marquetry, as here, was distinguished by its curved façade concealing pigeonholes and drawers. This superb example by Jacques Dubois, from the third quarter of the eighteenth century, bears a chinoiserie design on the cylinder fall. Kingwood is the major wood. The feet end in ormolu foliate sabots. *Parke-Bernet Galleries*

Left: Rococo brings the *ébéniste*'s skill to a peak in such choice marquetry as shown in the floral and fruit-laden branches in this cartouche-shaped panel decorating the side of a mid eighteenth-century commode. The projecting corner mount shows how intricate ormolu work matched the curve of the sinuously shaped cabinetwork of the period. *Parke-Bernet Galleries*

But the commode was the true star of the drawing room in this period. One major difference between the Régence commode and the Louis XV commode is that on the latter version the total treatment of the façade is all-important. The divisions between the drawers becomes almost imperceptible, hidden purposefully by the skillful *ébéniste* who treats the front as if it were a curved solid panel.

Commodes with drawers or doors were generally placed under trumeaus in eighteenth-century drawing rooms and designed to complement the boiserie. Another design determined by both the scale and height of the woodwork was the *bas d'armoire,* a low cupboard, designed to reach the top of the dado and to be placed between two windows or doors.

Of all antiques today, none commands higher prices than Louis XV and Louis XVI. Ever since World War II, when French furnishings began to capture the imagination of serious collectors, prices have skyrocketed. Although much remains from the period, it seems that everything that appears on the block or in shops is sold forthwith—especially if the design is choice or the price is moderate.

In this field moderate means low in four figures for small tables, $700 or more for bergères, $550 and up for fauteuils, $1,400 for a canapé in good condition (a nonperiod design might cost $300 to $400). As for table desks, one must expect to pay $1,500 for a writing table but high in four figures for a complete table desk, $700 and well up into four figures for a poudreuse, $1,000 and more for a good if not choice commode, $275 into four figures for a corner cupboard, $2,500 for a *secrétaire à abattant.*

Copies of French eighteenth-century are almost as common as modern pieces in today's shops. Many of the finer designs were conceived as matching pieces for existing antiques from the turn of the century on, and many were made as copies from the 1920's on. Since fine eighteenth-century French furniture in mint condition rarely shows age the way the early Renaissance and Gothic furnishings do, amateurs are advised to deal with reliable dealers or auction houses when making purchases in the period.

Better still, those with an eye for the sinuous curve but a pocketbook that does not quite match the finest cabinetmakers' prices, might consider the so-called French provincial furnishings. Many of these designs were made for aristocrats for their châteaus, and most will probably prove more suitable in today's home than the more elegant products of the *ébénistes'* workshop.

FRENCH PROVINCIAL

In its narrow sense, French provincial means the château and country furniture made during the eighteenth century. But in a broader sense it encompasses all furniture made from the seventeenth into the nineteenth century far from the sophisticated workshops of city-based craftsmen. A major misconception of those who are just becoming familiar with antiques is that French provincial

Provincial designs of the Louis XIV period remain as appealing today as in the day when the squared silhouette, block feet and shaped apron were in fashion at the close of the seventeenth century. This painted pale yellow chest with blue trim dates from around 1700. *Philip Colleck*

is synonymous with rustic furniture. Quite the contrary, French provincial is frequently as sophisticated in conception as that from an *ébéniste's* shop, but far less formal and finished. Its woods are less choice, its decoration far less likely to involve metal mounts, exotic inlays, wood marquetry and mechanical devices.

Châteaus flourished like vineyards in the countryside of France in the eighteenth century. Inside their stone walls, rooms exuded a different form of living than in the palaces closer to Paris. Comfort, ease, a life devoted to the pleasures of the hunt, gardening and a quieter pace were what the aristocrats sought away from the king's court of Versailles. And the burgeoning merchant and middle class, depending on the amount of their wealth and tastes, also determined that they would emulate Madame de Pompadour in matters of fashion and interior decoration.

This dichotomy between the two worlds in which French nobles moved exists today and has stirred as much interest in the French provincial styles as in the formal designs of eighteenth-century France. The late twentieth-century aristocrats of business and finance, both here and abroad, seek the same relaxation and often the same provincial furnishings to help achieve it as their highborn predecessors of the ancien régime.

The distinctive charm of French provincial furniture can be seen in the variety of chairs. The seventeenth century gave us columnar-based and turned-leg chairs that were modified in scale and less grand in embellishments than those made for palaces. The Louis XIV and Régence provincial fauteuils had the same motifs, but the carving on the frames and aprons is thicker in its chiseling than palace examples. The provincial cane backs and seats on side and corner chairs

Right: Cane was a favorite material in Louis XV provincial seating, as shown in this marquise. The painted off-white and lime-green trimmed settee, circa 1755, is carved with floral and foliate designs on the cabriole legs, shaped apron, arms and shaped crest rail. *Richard V. Hare*

Left: A painted white corner chair of the Louis XV style, circa 1730, has the modest carving in the scroll arm ends and on the apron and feet which distinguishes it from the palace examples. The caned back and seat, covered here by a cushion, were popular in château furnishings of that day. *Richard V. Hare*

hardly disguise the less shapely leg, the simplicity of the foliate carving. But the effect is rarely gross, and most often quite charming, and on occasion even amusing.

The Louis XV bergère is a little lower and more squat, covered in gaily patterned and colored chintz. It is an eminently comfortably easy chair. Ladder-back chairs, called *chaises à capucine,* were made with Louis XVI turned legs and later straighter uncarved legs in the style of the early nineteenth century. The woven straw seats and the uneven painting on the legs, stretchers and stiles, made these among the most popular. In their simplest form they are still being made today.

The "country-made" chairs of the Louis XVI period bore reeding, rosettes, medallion backs and finialed stiles less refined than city-made versions. But there is still an enviable grace in the total effect.

The armoires of France rise tall, the pride of every woman's trousseau and treasured by her throughout her lifetime. These double-doored cupboards, in spite of their imposing size, are very much in demand today as outsized dressers or cabinets used to store clothing, high-fidelity components and television sets.

Many so-called provincial designs were surprisingly decorative, employing, as here, black lacquer decoration in the Chinese taste and a *rouge royale* marble top with molded border. This mid eighteenth-century commode was probably made for use in a château. *Parke-Bernet Galleries*

The panetière, or livery cupboard that was later used to store bread, as well as the kneading trough and the étagère, are constant reminders of the delight the French have always shown in the pleasures of the table and furnishings used to display the wares used in dining.

Beds of the eighteenth century were no longer a rarity in châteaus and middle-class homes. The outsized cupboard-like bed of the era, called the lit clos, came, like the armoire, with the exchange of marriage vows. Its wood sides and shuttered or spindled doors provided both privacy in the one-room houses and protective walls to shield sleepers against chilly winter blasts. Other doorless beds with an upper story and tester designs, called *lits à colonnes,* were draped with fabric to attain the same effect.

Commodes and cupboards abound in mid to late eighteenth-century design. Sometimes these storage furnishings combined the rococo curves of Louis XV with the carved decoration of Louis XVI. The later the piece, the closer it is to the neoclassic vocabulary of decoration but not necessarily to its silhouette. The rounded corners, the cabriole leg—no matter how simple or primitively carved—the serpentine façade and the scrolls and volutes remain.

Some of the many designs include the tall buffets with open shelves at top, and two doors below. There are double-decker buffets with doors closing both the upper and lower sections. Low buffets with two or three doors, sometimes surmounted with a set-back upper section that was fitted with drawers to store eating utensils, were made in abundance. Sideboards came later and were equipped with marble tops and brass galleries. The Louis XVI buffets with open shelves at the sides, marble top and drawers for silver were made in the Provençal region until the end of the eighteenth century.

In French provincial furnishings one must expect to pay $300 and up for those of moderate quality, less for more primitive or rustic examples. Tables start at about $350, corner cabinets from $400, and *bureau plat*–type desks from about $500. Provincial commodes, like the small pair of Louis XVI designs in kingwood, may well rise to $1,900 or more. But there are less imposing examples available from about $500 up.

LOUIS XVI

France in the late eighteenth century was a nation torn intellectually and socially by the writings of Rousseau and Voltaire, sapped of its moral fiber by political and religious strife, and impoverished by the excessive spending of Louis XV and his court, which brought unbearable burdens of taxation to every man.

The nation was tiring of watching the merry-go-round that whirled dizzily to the rhythm of the life style of Louis XV and his favorites, Madame de Pompadour and, later, Madame du Barry. Whatever riches this period left to the world in the decorative arts, it took from the mouths and souls of the

A Louis XV provincial chest of drawers in fruitwood is modestly carved and decorated with ormolu in the handles and escutcheons, and stands on short scroll feet. *Parke-Bernet Galleries*

Régence-Louis XV table desk in walnut has a serpentine front and a gracefully molded apron housing one wide drawer. The cabriole legs end in hoof feet on this design dating from about 1745. *Richard V. Hare*

Right: A Louis XV provincial tabouret in walnut, standing on heavy but gracefully curved cabriole legs ending in scrolls, has a shaped serpentine apron on four sides. *Richard V. Hare*

Left: A Louis XV lacquered *table de thé* in a provincial design that combines the simplicity of silhouette and the bright green lacquer and finely chiseled sabots more typical of palace furniture of the day. *Richard V. Hare (Taylor and Dull photo)*

common people. Payment would come in blood and revolution, but not until after another decorative arts style was nurtured into being and a score of skilled craftsmen had contributed their talents in developing neoclassicism to new heights. In furnishings at least, the prophecy attributed to Louis XV, *"Après nous le déluge,"* would be delayed in its fulfillment long enough for the new vocabulary of design to be developed.

Louis XVI, physically and mentally incapable of turning the tides that Louis XV had set in motion, came to the throne in 1774. His equally immature wife, Marie Antoinette, would turn her back on the tumult that surrounded the king's throne during the fifteen years of her husband's reign to play the part of the dairymaid, walking in the gardens surrounding her hamlet at Versailles. These royal attitudes, set against the background of the turbulent social scene, produced a decorative arts style as unreal, as gracious and as refined and pretty as the reigning monarchs themselves.

In every art movement there exists the momentum that thrusts it forward, and, more important in this case, the seeds of its own demise. The rococo style of Louis XV was no exception. As history has proven over and over again, some outside force always seems to speed the conclusion of one style and the emergence of another in rapid succession.

The return of classicism to furniture in the late eighteenth century was a natural æsthetic reaction to the excesses of the rococo style. It would have come, albeit slower, even if Herculaneum and Pompeii had remained forever buried under the layers of ashes and lava that had obliterated these historic cities seventeen centuries earlier. For some years, in fact, craftsmen had argued that the curved lines of the rococo produced furniture that was not structurally sound.

But these rediscoveries of the ancient cities did occur in 1738 and 1753. Overcome with ennui at the seemingly endless curves, the sinuous silhouettes and the froth and fantasy that no longer amused quite so much, the French began to see anew the special charm of the straightened leg, the classical orders of architecture, the decorative repertory of motifs derived from the ancient myths of gods and goddesses.

The archaeologists uncovered rich treasures of Roman furnishings. What the Renaissance Italians had sometimes had to imagine from the ruins that surrounded them in the streets of Rome, the French eighteenth-century cabinet-makers could see in three dimensions, or at least abstract from contemporary engravings or the vestiges in painted decorations on early vases.

Chairs and tables at which these Romans had dined, *torchères* that lit their rooms, couches or beds on which they reclined, emerged from the ruins. What had been swallowed in the heat of the volcano, sparked new life in late eighteenth-century French and other furniture.

Books, reports from travelers and most important of all the engravings of Giovanni Battista Piranesi, the Italian artist, made known the resurrected beauties of ancient Rome to "modern" France. Louis XV still sat on the throne in 1768. In that year Le Petit Trianon, designed for Madame de Pompadour, who had died four years earlier, was completed in the neoclassic style we now call Louis XVI. In that day, however, it was referred to as the *à la grecque* style. The king's favorite, Madame du Barry, moved into this architectural jewel in 1768 upon its completion.

Most experts date the beginning of neoclassicism in furnishings at 1760. A decade would pass before the impact of its sobering influence would be fully felt. Two cultures separated by three centuries had looked at some of the same Roman ruins and developed two extremely different art movements. The

A Louis XVI commode with unusual side cupboards bears the classical fluted legs and ormolu mounts. The bold rosette drawer pulls and bow-topped escutcheons on this mahogany design signed by Fidelis Schey are also typical of the neoclassic mode. *Philip Colleck*

French would certainly extol the more modern style in any comparison between Italian Renaissance and Louis XVI. The gracious, less imposing, more refined classical designs that grew out of this later age, an era already accustomed to creature comforts, tested the *ébénistes'* skills to their limits, and these skilled artisans were not found wanting.

The roster of names of *ébénistes* who molded the Louis XVI furniture style is the most impressive of any period anywhere. It included Claude Charles Saunier, Jules Leleu, Martin Carlin, Adam Weisweiler, Guillaume Beneman and the greatest *ébéniste* of all—Jean Henri Riesener. David Roentgen, like Riesener and Weisweiler, was German, but the mechanical genius, who was a master of marquetry, was considered a cabinetmaker, not an *ébéniste*. Roentgen's work was heavier, more German than French, and he maintained his workshop in Neuwied on the Rhine.

The major characteristics of the Louis XVI style were the replacement of the rococo curve with the neoclassic straight line, light and delicate proportions and rectangular silhouettes. The woods favored were either such grained ones as acajou (mahogany), out of fashion during the Louis XV period, or ebony. Painted furniture in pale hues and more subtle combinations, replaced the richer palette of the previous period. Lacquerwork declined, but other French techniques of decoration—carving, marquetry, ormolu and painted panels—persisted through to the end of this period.

The handbook of ornament at this time was replete with classical details that had recurred throughout history with a few late eighteenth-century innovations added. Colonnettes and pilasters stud the façades of chests, commodes, and desks, and form the legs and stiles of chests and sofas. Floral motifs—roses and garlands of flowers—are prominently used along with ribbon bowknots, festoons, lyres, Cupid's bows and darts, acanthus leaves and arabesques. Porcelain inlay and Wedgewood plaques appear on the finest cabinetmakers' works. In the latter part of the period, Egyptian, Greek and Etruscan motifs appear in furniture, inspired by the many books on the subject of antique cultures that appeared around 1780.

Naturally the changes did not come overnight or en masse. In the evolution of Louis XVI furnishings there is a slow straightening of the cabriole leg after sixty years of dominance as the support for all furnishings. And the classical idiom finally adopted is never as strict as the models of the Greco-Roman furnishings entombed for centuries under crusts of molten rock.

Chairs in the Louis XVI period definitely become straighter, more angular. But the curve of Louis XV remains in the slightly rounded back, seat and arms—characteristic of the comfort that French aristocrats and wealthy citizens demanded. Gone is the free-flowing line, and in its place comes the return of visible joints separating the leg from the arm or back support or its seat. If these changes brought a lessening in comfort, they brought a return to a sense of æsthetic order.

Fauteuils were executed with both medallion and rectangular backs, edged with classical moldings. The rectangular back is not composed with completely straight lines. Some have concave curves framing a straight top rail, rounded endings called volutes on arms, concave curves in arm supports and rounded joints between legs and seats.

Armchairs with padded arm rests, called *manchettes,* were joined without setbacks to the legs. However, while women wore the puffy overskirts called panniers, the arm supports on fauteuils were curved inward to allow women to sit comfortably without their skirts being bunched awkwardly by the supports of the chair arms. Later, when fashion decreed a change in dress, the baluster arm support appeared. Chair legs were rarely square, but vertical and rounded, tapering toward the ankle with vertical or spiral fluting carved out from the gorge, or concave molding, to the foot.

The bergère, like the fauteuil, succumbed to the columnar leg and the rosette covering the leg and seat joints. The only difference between these chairs, as in early times, is the upholstery filling the space between arm and seat; sometimes, a lower, deeper cast was given the bergère to increase comfort.

The splat-back chair, introduced in England in the late seventeenth century, appears in French furniture for the first time in the late eighteenth century.

Left: The drum table, a design that would take on military overtones in the Directoire period, was another favorite shape of the transitional Louis XV–XVI period. This marquetry design has a top inlaid with various woods and mother-of-pearl with an amusing pseudo-Chinese landscape and a door decorated with a vase of flowers. The circular tray table is also inlaid on a sycamore ground. *Parke-Bernet Galleries*

Right: In this transitional *bibliothèque* one can see in the legs how the cabriole curve has been gradually straightened between the Louis XV and Louis XVI styles. The squarer silhouette of this small, eminently simple tulipwood storage unit and the modest use of ormolu in the cabochon centering the apron and the foliate sabots on the feet are typical of the changes in the third quarter of the eighteenth century. *Parke-Bernet Galleries*

Georges Jacob is credited with the innovation of the pierced lyre splat, a form that had been reserved for clocks and candleholders until then. His lyre-backed chairs were considered quite exclusive and commanded high prices in their time, as they do now. The same can be said of chairs with sheaf-of-wheat backs and those in a balloon shape, a motif inspired by the first balloon flight of the brothers Montgolfier in 1783. Dubbed *chaise à l'anglaise,* all these chairs were gilded, painted or wrought in solid mahogany.

Other seating designs included the ubiquitous *pliants,* those X-form folding stools, as well as sofas, canapés and daybeds. The changes that came in this period in larger seating designs are few. Canapés are sometimes larger, with triangular end seats separated from the main sofa by arms. These are called *à confidente.* Four-poster beds, the *lit à colonnes,* returned to fashion. And the tester beds surmounted by a domed canopy (*lit à la polonaise*) or a rectangular canopy (*lit à la duchesse*) that was attached to the ceiling were also in favor.

The most extravagant beds were decorated with generous portions of the full repertory of carved decoration—helmets, shields, fluting, columns, pine-cone finials, clusters or arrows, medallions and Cupid's bows.

The most visible change in tables, aside from the classical silhouettes, is the wood used. Mahogany tables are abundant and were designed with greater simplicity, allowing the beauty of the wood to dominate the façade. Unlike the rococo tables, where often the hardware seems hidden, the hardware on

Left: Louis XVI bergère, with a gondola-shaped back, is a low, wide beechwood design. It has padded arms, curved and fluted supports, a bowed front rail carved with cabbage roses, and it stands on short round, tapered and fluted legs. *Parke-Bernet Galleries*

Right: The rectangular backs and the padded armrests on fluted urn supports of this Louis XVI fauteuil are typical of the late eighteenth-century style. Legs are fluted and tapering and topped by paterae. *Parke-Bernet Galleries*

Louis XVI tables is purposely decorative. Ormolu wreaths or rosette pulls, beading banding drawers, brass galleries edging tabletops and shelves—all stand out sharply against the rich brown wood.

Another change evident in neoclassic furniture is the stretcher, gone through-

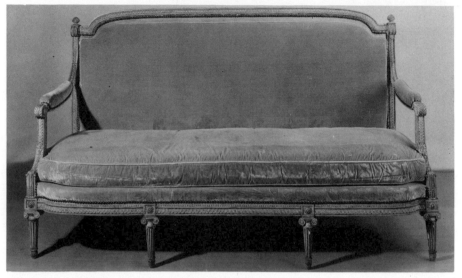

Above: Louis XVI canapé standing on legs carved with Ionic capitals is a painted white seating design. The flat back is bordered with an arched top rail carved with guilloche and beading with the side uprights topped by pomegranate finials. *Parke-Bernet Galleries*

Below: This late Louis XVI painted green and gilded sofa with a shaped back rising high on one end is carved in the classical taste with scrolling foliage, paterae and quivers of arrows. *Parke-Bernet Galleries*

Above left: Oval occasional table of the Louis XVI period has a gilded bronze border and three-quarter gallery edging the top. The top drawer is fitted with a leather-lined writing surface. The platform joining the legs is kidney-shaped. *Philip Colleck*

Above right: Louis XVI architect's table shows the mechanical ingenuity of late eighteenth-century French cabinet-makers. A double ratchet top, fitted slides at the sides and a fitted drawer are supported by squared and tapering legs. *Philip Colleck*

Right: Modest touches of ormolu appear at the capitals, on the legs and apron of this *secrétaire à abattant*. The kingwood design conceals a maroon-lined writing surface behind the fall front. A mottled gray marble slab serves as the top. *Parke-Bernet Galleries*

out the Louis XV period, but necessary again to join straight chair legs and lyre-shaped table supports.

On secretaries, marquetry was the favorite decorative treatment. Musical instruments and flowers were the most frequently recurring themes in this inlay work. Ormolu, of more modest size and subject matter than previously, is used sparingly on the stiles and aprons of most *secrétaires à abattant*. But toward the close of the Louis XVI reign, there is a return to heavier, richer pieces, to commodes of monumental size and heavy mounts very like those of the Louis XIV period. It is as though the cabinetmakers, like their clients, are having their one last fling before dissolution.

Louis XVI designs command lower prices than Louis XV, but they are still rarely moderate, and the finest examples skyrocket in price. Fauteuils may be $375 up. At a recent sale a pair of signed Jacob chairs went for $1,900, more than double the price of good unsigned chairs.

Side chairs are less expensive, starting at about $100 each, especially when there is some doubt as to the age. But medium to fine examples will certainly cost $500 or more. Settees bring $425 up and beds about $500 into four figures.

Tables with drawers may be as low as $300, but most command higher prices —$500 and up. Modest commodes bring $450 at their lowest prices, but for finer examples the bottom price is $550. Any with a proven history, as the commode from the Château de Chatelup, near Tours, that had its original château mark and sold recently for $3,200, will be in four figures.

Desks are very much in demand today. Mahogany cylinder-type bureaus, for instance, will be $800 and up. A *secrétaire à abattant* costs from $700 into four figures. Fine, flat-topped writing tables may start at $700 but those with inlay of porcelain plaques bring over $2,000.

DIRECTOIRE

Even the French Revolution of 1789 did not immediately affect or quicken the pace of furniture evolution. The Directoire style is a transitional period lasting from 1790 to 1804, during which Louis XVI remains a dominant spirit. But ever increasing interest in antiquity slowly alters the lightness of neoclassic silhouettes of the ancien régime, moving it toward the weightier Empire period. A third influence shaping furnishings of the era was the increased use of mechanical methods to produce furniture for the burgeoning middle class.

The decorative arts period takes its name from the Directory, or government of directors that remained in power from 1795 to 1799. The designation "Directoire" merely separates the neoclassicism begun thirty years earlier from that produced under the new wave of patriotism and nostalgia for antiquity that followed the Reign of Terror. There is, of course, an increasing acknowledgment of the power of the farmer in these years. The most loyal of cabinetmakers erased all patterns and designs from their work that might summon up memories of the ancien régime.

As in every period—and particularly those eras that mark transitions—the Directoire style has two strong characteristics. There are echoes and precursor motifs. Delicate carving from the past continued, if somewhat coarser, and the total effect is neither as restrained nor as elegant as in the decades before the Revolution. On the other hand there is the lively evidence of new ideas. In this case it is the threefold stylistic fancies for antiquity, for Gallic military and social themes and for agricultural motifs.

The new themes exist more in the decorative motifs than in any innovative total shaping of furniture. But some elements, like the backward roll of the top rail of a chair back and the outward curve of arms on chairs, signal the deeper commitment to Grecian forms. Furniture began to look more Greek than Greek, more Roman than Roman. Actually, from 1780 on, sparked by a series of classical-oriented works on art and architecture, Greek, Etruscan and Egyptian motifs began permeating furniture design. Sphinxes, hawks, sarcophagi, the palm, the lotus, and fretwork were increasingly used in ornamental details.

Under Jacques Louis David, one of the signers of Louis XVI's death warrant, antique themes flourished. The painter propagated the style through the furniture he created in his canvases from which the decorative artists and *ébénistes* took inspiration. The craftsmen dug deeper into the past for classical forms to inspire them further. The Greek klismos, the curule seating forms and the daybed on which David painted Madame de Récamier would all come to life

Directoire fauteuil in mahogany, covered in dark green Moroccan leather with gold tooled trimming, anticipates the Empire period in its squared back and curved crest rail. Signed Jacob Frères, Rue Meslée. *Richard V. Hare*

in such capable hands as the elder Georges Jacob, the cabinetmaker, as well as Charles Percier and Pierre-François-Leonard Fontaine, architects and designers.

The patriotic themes were shortlived. From the last days of the Revolution up to the opening days of the Directory, such new motifs occurred as drums, spears, stars, trumpets, Phrygian or liberty caps and clasped hands, a symbol of fraternity. Agricultural symbols—sheaves of wheat, the plow, scythe and flail remained longer. But then as the nation began to revive, to reopen its workshops and attempt once again to create commerce that would help to restore the nation's economy, thoughts of the Revolution which had left the nation broken and bleeding, faded. The *ébénistes* were only too happy to put such thoughts aside. But those artisans who had not left their workshops during the hard years of the Revolution to enter other fields, found changes in their profession. Now there was a disorganized apprentice system, a break in the high standards of traditional French craftsmanship, and fewer aristocratic clients to serve. The guillotine had wounded, but not killed the decorative arts.

All these new influences shaped chairs that had either straight front legs, as had been seen for decades in provincial furniture, topped by Grecian foliate carvings, or that set on outcurving front legs and canting rear legs. The marquetry star centering the top rail, the carved Egyptian or Greek head appearing at the top of a leg, arm posts shaped like sphinxes and the human or animalistic

A banquette showing the Directoire-Louis XVI style has a low, outcurved back, vasiform uprights terminating in leaf-scroll ornament. The fluted, round and tapering legs are echoes of the earlier style that Jacob Desmalter made about 1805. Painted French gray, highlighted in vibrant green. *Parke-Bernet Galleries*

feet are but a few of the ways antiquity showed itself in this period. It is not uncommon on chairs or other furnishings to see stronger colors than were used under Louis XVI. One of the most distinctive color combinations of the period was scarlet, white and blue, a reflection of the patriotic spirit, for these were the colors of the republic's flag.

Daybeds, among the most characteristic pieces of the era, bore medallions of ormolu on their wood frames. These frequently depicted Greek gods and goddesses, classical heads of women, lyres, amphorae and butterflies. Sides curved outward in a form reminiscent of the klismos. The daybed appeared in many guises—with two arms of equal height, as in the painting of Madame de Récamier by David, with sides of unequal height with the headrest higher than the footboard, with a back joining the sides whether they be of equal or unequal height. Beds too, but to a lesser extent, bore modish characteristics. Crested headboards with low-pitched, pedimented shaping appeared, and in some cases the stiles flared outward at the top.

Very little difference is seen in the commodes and writing furnishings of the time. But tables in most cases are round, with marble tops supported by pedestal or tripod bases that show the rage for antique themes both in the circular form and in the motifs decorating the base. Wrought iron and bronze furniture in the Greek manner also appeared in this period.

Prices for furniture produced in this epoch approximate those of the Louis XVI period. A pair of bergères recently sold in New York City for $600, and

Directoire small *bureau plat,* with a top panel of green leather bordered in mahogany and framed with ormolu, stands on square tapering legs ending in box sabots. *Parke-Bernet Galleries*

a set of six side chairs and one armchair for dining was $750. A signed Claude Chapuis dining table, extending from forty-seven inches in length to five feet five inches, sold for a remarkably low price of $1,000. But a small *bureau plat* brought, as expected, $1,300, and a commode, $550. Small tables of this period are as popular as those of the preceding era and command prices from $700 and well into four figures.

A late Directoire console, circa 1810, is mahogany decorated with brass inlay and topped with marble. The diamond-shaped inlays at the corners, the shaped legs and feet and the rectilinear silhouette are typical of the period. *Philip Colleck*

chapter 5

ENGLAND
Queen Anne through Sheraton

~§ If the Queen Anne period (1702–14) did not produce any striking innovations in furniture design, it did leave the world one of the most beautiful and satisfying furniture forms ever created. The splat-back chair, introduced in the last years of the seventeenth century, evolved to perfection before 1715. No chair that followed it in the eighteenth century, regarded as the golden age of English cabinetmaking, surpassed it in beauty of form and simplicity. The chair and all the refinements of the period happened in spite of the monarch, not because of her. Actually she was neither influential on nor interested in the development of the decorative arts.

England was still absorbing and developing baroque ideas as the eighteenth century opened on the reign of the last of the Stuarts. Curved forms, the scrolls, cabriole legs, the undulating fiddleback splat, the top rails and seats continued and were mastered with refinement.

Lacquerwork was all the rage in early eighteenth-century London when this side chair decorated in gold and black was created. The splat back and the pierced crest rail of the Queen Anne chair, which stands on gracefully curved cabriole legs ending in hoof feet, are other choice characteristics. *Philip Colleck*

Incorporating comfort in furniture became of increasing concern to the cabinetmakers who tried to satisfy the ever more luxurious and sophisticated tastes of the English aristocracy. Upholstered chairs were designed to conform more closely to the natural shape of the human body. The back of the simple Queen Anne splat-back with its upholstered seat, was made slightly lower than the William and Mary chairs and slightly concave at shoulder height. Settees and wing chairs were also developed to their zenith in this period. These settees were often like multiple chairs with two, three or four chair backs joined.

As always happens after periods of great surface enrichment on furniture, there is a strong reaction bringing simplicity back into focus. The Queen Anne period saw the rejection of the type of flamboyant carving that had characterized seventeenth-century furniture. What carving there was became delicate and was used with restraint. The shell and acanthus on the knees of cabriole legs, the fluted pilasters are subdued expressions of the carver's skills.

Wood—walnut and fine veneers—are handled with judicious regard for the most salient and beautiful characteristics of the woods themselves. Japanned surfaces continued to appeal to the populace throughout the Queen Anne period. But the back- or red- and gold-lacquered secretaries, chairs, tables and dressing tables are far fewer in number than the plainer walnut or veneered designs of that day.

In the Queen Anne period, chairmaking became a specialized craft. Prior to this time the talents of the joiner, the upholsterer, the turner and the carver were required in making a fine chair. Now one man shapes the cabriole leg with its club, hoof, or spade foot, carving the knees with shell or acanthus, modeling the fiddleback and frame, fitting or dropping in the upholstered seat that was covered most often in needlework, velvet or leather.

Later the splat back was pierced, and shell motifs were used on such other parts of the chair as the front center of the seat frame and the middle of the top rail. The club foot eventually disappeared and was replaced by the Chinese dragon's claw, grasping a ball, the Oriental pearl of wisdom.

Queen Anne side chairs mark a high point in the evolution of chairs for another reason. Gone are the stretchers that joined the cabriole legs of the late seventeenth-century splat-back chairs. After 1708 the stretcher became obsolete. Only on library chairs are the stretchers necessary, because added strength was required to support the sitter and his book. This narrow-backed design, also called a cockfight chair, had an armrest for a top rail that was centered by an easel on which a book was placed. There was a drawer under the seat, and the chair was straddled backward.

Prices on English Queen Anne chairs are not nearly so high as on American versions. Interpretations of the style made in Portugal, Italy and Holland are even less expensive. A good English side chair commands $200, but the finest examples rise to four figures. A set of eight black-lacquered English chairs recently sold for $1,750. Period armchairs can be found at from $375—a price lower than what it would cost to copy one today.

Wing chairs in the Queen Anne period surpass both the seventeenth-century and the late eighteenth-century designs in appearance. The concentration on refining the silhouettes of chairs brought cabinetmakers to create the continuously curved back, wing and arm characteristic of this period. On later chairs the wings look like awkward appurtenances applied as afterthoughts. Queen Anne wing chairs, rare today because upholstery was not in abundance in the period and because this so-called "easy" chair seldom withstood the heavy demands as the favorite chair, can be found for about $1,000 and up. Early in 1969 a fine one sold for $2,200.

Equally graceful are the upholstered armchairs with open sides. The arm, curving from the back, swinging outward and in again in an S-curve, is shaped into a crook arm and downward in a reverse curve to the seat. An important functional note is the flattened portion on the back of the arm where the elbows could be rested comfortably. A rare and particularly fine example of this type sold for $1,800 recently. Less distinguished examples will cost considerably less.

Like the *pliant* in France, the folding stool popular from the medieval period through the eighteenth century, the upholstered, four-legged stool was found in every middle-class to better English household. Cabriole legs, needlepoint-covered seats in square, oval or round shapes were made. Those extant are extremely desirable and may cost as much as $950 or more.

In spite of the many technical advances made in the era, it was still necessary to use more than four legs under the needlework-covered settees. Few of these sofas measured more than four feet in length. The rounded backs slope down into the arms. Seats are covered with a single long pillow.

Game tables, made in England from the late Middle Ages, became one of the most important furnishings of eighteenth-century households. Chess and backgammon, played for two centuries in castles and manor homes, continued to have great importance. But cards and gambling became the most important form of entertainment. Reversible tops on tables showed a checkerboard on one side, a backgammon board on the other. Card tables painted with scenes, or covered with needlework showing people playing cards, or finished with green felt, were the fashion. There were dished corners for candlesticks, sunken cups for money, and fold-over tops so that the tables could be placed against the wall. They were made in both round and rectangular versions. Today game tables are moderate in price, costing from $700 up.

Side tables, although not innovative, were made in great numbers, and today they can be found at $200 or $300. Those with any distinction range from $1,000.

The toilet or dressing table of the early eighteenth century, like that in France, became an important furnishing because of the custom of women receiving visitors in their bedroom. More often than not, it appears without a desk portion at the back. But many were surmounted and framed by curtaining. A dressing table that was little more than a black lacquer mirror set on a base with one drawer sold recently for $425. But a good dressing table would probably cost $1,500 or more today. Even one of recent vintage in the style is liable

The growing interest in cards quickened the cabinet-makers to oblige in the early years of the Queen Anne era. Here a walnut card table, veneered with burled wood on top, has rounded corners that when open serve as candle wells. The shell-carved knees on the cabriole legs and the shaped squarish feet show a master's hand. *Parke-Bernet Galleries*

to command from $400. Strangely enough, in a recent auction both an undistinguished original and a fine twentieth-century copy sold for the same price—$400.

Teatime had settled in as a custom by the Queen Anne period, and tables were designed with which to enjoy the ritual. Because tea was still costly, the entire tea was made at the tea table. The servant brought the kettle of boiling water, placed it on a tripod-based, brass or pierced wood table that was triangular-shaped with a gallery-framed top. Then she stood by while her mistress took the tea from the caddy, placed it in the pot and poured the water—and when the tea was ready she poured it.

Whether the beverage was tea, coffee or chocolate, the English were prepared with a table to serve it on. The tilt-top, piecrust and gallery-topped tables of the time multiplied. Prices start from about $700.

Tablewares were made in great number in the early eighteenth century and so were the china cabinets to contain them. Not only aristocrats but also the middle classes collected chinaware, making everyone "a judge of teapots and dragons," according to a critic of the day. A typical oak Welsh dresser, that precursor of the sideboard, brings about $475 today.

Highboys continued in popularity and were made with a scroll or broken pediment. Narrow bookcases with glazed doors and astragal bars were made in imitation of one that Samuel Pepys was said to have owned. Fall-front desks, known as bureaus, began to be used in bedrooms. Secretaries with bookcases at the top, called bureau cabinets, appeared in greater numbers in other, more public rooms. One beautifully proportioned walnut bureau of this kind, with a sloping fall-front and a masterfully fitted interior of drawers and pigeonholes, brought $2,600 recently. More modest ones at lower prices are available. Another fall-front bureau cabinet with an arched top and bracket feet sold for $2,500 recently.

Chests of drawers often had fold-over tops in order to double as writing or toilet tables. Many chests, both the bachelor and the blanket kinds, in the early days of the eighteenth century, stood on bracket feet, and some were japanned and decorated in the Chinese style.

Although the Queen Anne period officially terminates with the death of the queen in 1714, the development of the furniture style continued through the George I period. One reason is that the arts flourished then not because of interest on the part of the monarch but because of the activities of the landed gentry in advancing the arts.

As in all periods, there was a time lag between the development of designs for the aristocrats and the adoption of such forms for the middle classes, and there was even a longer lapse before rural craftsmen took up the style. For these reasons the forms and elements of the Queen Anne style continued to be made through 1735, and in rural areas even later.

Modest proportions distinguish this Queen Anne
walnut bureau cabinet from larger ones of the era.
The upper part is surmounted by an arched and
molded cornice broken at the center and inlaid with
a shell motif. The lower section has a sloping fall
front concealing a nest of drawers, and stands on
bracket feet. *Parke-Bernet Galleries*

Fall front bureau of the Queen Anne period is a choice, small desk of the period. As is typical, the interior is fitted with small drawers and a green baize writing tablet. It stands on bracket feet. *Parke-Bernet Galleries*

PALLADIAN

Lord Burlington was the man most responsible in the early 1720's for a revival of the classical mode as practiced in the sixteenth century by Andrea Palladio in Italy and by Inigo Jones in England a century later. It was Lord Burlington who introduced the architect William Kent to his aristocratic friends. Kent, who had lived in Italy and shared Burlington's enthusiasm for Palladio, became the first English designer to conceive of furniture as an architectural element in rooms.

Kent's furniture designs were massive, boxy and lavishly embellished with carved decoration in pilasters, pediments, pendants, acanthus, gadrooning—all the architectural and decorative trappings of the Italian High Renaissance. The only elements out of harmony were the recurring cabriole legs. There was sound reasoning for Kent's frequent and generous use of gilt. The gold finish warmed the interiors of the rooms they adorned.

William Kent is one of the first in a long line of architects and designers who publicized their work through books. In his *Gentleman's and Builder's Companion,* published in 1739, Kent offered designs for side tables, bookcases and cabinets.

Mahogany began to replace walnut after 1720 when France cut its exports in walnut and, a decade later, England repealed its heavy duty on West Indian mahogany. Mahogany would increase in demand after 1740 as the French rococo made deeper inroads into English thinking. For the lighter style could be modeled more easily in the stronger mahogany than in walnut. The larger size of the boards cut from the huge trees made it possible for dining-table tops to be made without veneering. Finally, mahogany was worm-resistant, whereas walnut was very susceptible.

The twenty-year hiatus for carvers, gilders, and decorative metalworkers drew to an end as furniture bowed to exuberance once again. From 1725 to 1735 the lion mask became commonplace on the knees of cabriole legs. The lion head, mane, paws and hocks appeared alone or combined with eagles or dolphins on all manner of furnishings. Then foliate, scroll, cherubic, shell, serpentine and animal carvings swept through furniture design.

Although the chairs of the period are far less memorable than the tables,

The influence of William Kent is readily apparent in this George II side table with an oblong top, wave-scroll frieze between pairs of reeded buttress-like legs that are carved with scallop shell cresting. The mahogany table stands on imposing block feet. From the Walter P. Chrysler, Jr. collection. *Parke-Bernet Galleries (Taylor and Dull photo)*

cabinets and desks, there are some that must not be overlooked. Furnishings for reception rooms were quite extraordinary. A chair by William Kent in the Venetian baroque manner was a carved and gilded fantasy combining serpent's heads as arm ends, an X-form base in front, canted legs at back and a pierced apron of shells and acanthus. The X form was also used for stools that differed from the French *pliants* not only in the amount of detail worked into the scroll elements and the shells joining the center of the X with the seat at front and back, but also in the ponderous effect.

The Queen Anne chair began changing in 1720. First the splat became decorated with, among other motifs, an acanthus leaf design. Later the splat was pierced or cut, as on one design where the splat stops a few inches short of the top rail and is joined to the stiles with carved wood. The seat of the Queen Anne chair widened. Front seat rails or aprons were also decorated with acanthus or shells. Legs thickened and soon seemed to have grown beards as the lion mane fashion developed and covered legs. Other chairs and settees were surmounted with crests on yokes at the center of the top rail. Legs in scroll shape were usually ornamented with masks, lion faces or Indian headdress.

A pair of small settees with rectangular seats and short roll-over arms, standing on six cabriole legs that end in short claw-and-ball feet, brought $3,250 recently. The choice needlework coverings were certainly part of the reason for the price. Otherwise prices are lower.

A variety of other chair types emerged in the second quarter of the eighteenth century, some of which appear to have particular meaning today for a number of reasons. The porter's chair, for instance, is a living-room conversation piece that would appeal to a number of collectors. If the chairs can be found, they will probably have prices far below their more serious and functional cousins of the same period. The porter's chair is a wood-framed design, generally surmounted by a wood hood or canopy, and with solid side panels to reduce drafts.

Corner and writing chairs are another interesting category. Although few people place such designs in the corners of rooms today, they continue to be very much in demand as extra seating in dens and even in informal living rooms. The most commonly found versions have four carved legs with shells on the knees, a back of two splats set between three vertical spindles and under low top rails. Prices begin at about $500, but for a moderately good to fine chair of this type, one must expect to pay $1,000.

The tall, narrow, Dutch-type secretary cabinets, introduced from Holland into England around 1700, were highly developed by 1730. The kettle or bombé bases show the evolution from the baroque. Whorl-ended pediments shaped in scrolls were centered by medallions or armorial designs. The upper section was a single-door cabinet flanked by pilasters. The desk section was concealed behind a drop-front drawer-like façade. Below it most secretaries had at least three drawers. The bureaus made under George I had sloping fall-fronts, fitted

Right: A rounded back for resting the arms, supported by three turned columns and two vasiform splats, and a rounded seat at back show how functional yet gracious early eighteenth-century English designs of George I period were. The cabriole legs end in pointed pad feet. *Parke-Bernet Galleries*

Below: Breakfront book cases, a specialty of the Georgian epoch, assumed grand proportions by the third quarter of the eighteenth century when this George III design was made. The mahogany example has a writing desk concealed behind two long drawers in the center. The upper section has thirteen-pane glass doors. *Parke-Bernet Galleries*

Above: By 1760 the three-pillar Georgian dining table echoed the neoclassic mode. The oval top, the massive tetrapod bases on castered feet and the additional concealed feature of swing arms instead of brass cleats to support the leaves make this a distinctive example. *Parke-Bernet Galleries*

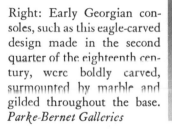

Right: Early Georgian consoles, such as this eagle-carved design made in the second quarter of the eighteenth century, were boldly carved, surmounted by marble and gilded throughout the base. *Parke-Bernet Galleries*

inside with drawers and pigeonholes with three large and two small drawers below. A simple but handsome example might cost $600 or more today.

The break-front bookcase also evolved in the Georgian era, assuming a vertical emphasis after 1740. The center section projected beyond the two sides with the entire lower part enclosed by doors, drawers or both. These architectural designs had plinth or bracket bases. A distinctive George II bookcase might be of mahogany or rosewood veneer, its upper portion surmounted by a broken pediment, and furnished with arched, wood-framed doors carved with swags of corn or flowers. The lower section might be banded at the top with a Greek key frieze, have doors and drawers framed by beading, acanthus carving, and shaped pilasters.

There was a great variety of small tables produced under George II, including those used as side tables for games and wine serving. A William Kent side table, for instance, would almost always be square, have a marble top and an apron frieze decorated with gadrooning and petal tips. Legs were often of corbel shape and carved with classical motifs. One of this type sold recently for $175 at auction, but most command higher prices in shops.

A George II mahogany card table with folding top, rounded outset corners, a baize-lined playing surface inside and a drawer in the frieze brought $400 not long ago. Wine tables of the era, although not common today, can be found with luck at moderate prices. Recently $400 was the price paid for a circular-topped, baluster-column and tripod-leg-based table from the period.

Early Georgian dining tables were of two kinds. The gateleg type had been introduced and was widely used in the Queen Anne period, continuing in fashion up to about 1740. But the newer mahogany designs were circular or oval tables with cabriole-legged bases. Two legs swung out to support the drop leaves on either side of the table.

Storage furniture in dining rooms did not begin to appear until the second quarter of the century. The tables found in dining rooms were almost exclusively used as serving tables or for display of dinnerwares. Such marble-topped sideboards were often of gilded wood, were elaborately carved according to the early Georgian fashion and of an imposing size. The less ornate designs of the late 1730's were mahogany. Carved details of acanthus leaves, shells, masks, Greek key-and-scroll motifs were more restrained.

Consoles were among the most distinctive designs of the era. They too had marble tops and monumental bases. Base designs of eagles with outspread wings standing on a rocky promontory, were destined to flourish beyond the period after other early Georgian innovations were discarded for newer fashions. A pair of superb carved gilt-wood consoles of this type were sold recently for $28,000. Another console made in the same period but without the eagle base brought $2,250.

CHIPPENDALE

It comes as a shock to neophyte collectors that the most illustrious name in cabinetmaking, possibly in all history, was not an innovator but an adaptor of past, and what were then current, styles. Thomas Chippendale, born in Yorkshire in 1718, learned the trade of joinery from his father, after whom he was named. The Chippendales are believed to have moved to London around 1727. By 1750, the younger Chippendale had a flourishing business in St. Martin's Lane.

Chippendale's fame rests to a great extent upon his book, *The Gentleman and Cabinet-Maker's Director,* a trade catalog of 1754 that was slightly revised in 1755 and enlarged again in 1762. But, as is now believed, his real creative talents lay not in the furniture designs shown in the *Director,* as well as those that flowed in a stunning variety from his workshops, but in his business genius in organizing and selling. The real creators of the furniture designs are now believed to have been cabinetmakers in his employ. But if Chippendale did not create the highly eclectic designs that bear his name, he was certainly fully responsible for the popularity of his books, for the selling of his designs to aristocrats for use in their fine London houses and on their country estates, and for the superior quality of all furnishings emanating from his workshops.

The meld of styles in the *Director* is impressive. The baroque, early Georgian designs were on the wane long before Chippendale became a name to be reckoned with in cabinetmaking. In its place Chinese, rococo and Gothic, combined with the still-fashionable Palladian style, took precedence.

The Chinese mode in England had been popular since the close of the seventeenth century, when trade with the East and books on japanning techniques had made their mark on the William and Mary and Queen Anne styles. In the mid eighteenth century lacquered furnishings were still very much in favor, but the influence of the Chinese style spread to the carving and shaping of furniture as cabinetmakers became more enamored of Chinese architectural details.

New in furniture in this era are the pagoda tops on bookcases, cabinets, beds and even chairs, where they appeared as the crest of the top rail. Latticework

Right: George III bureau-china cabinet in the Chinese taste is a superb example of the pierced and carved fretwork so popular in the third quarter of the eighteenth century. This rare example, attributed to William Vile, has a drop-front writing section masked as two drawers. The mahogany design stands on square, paneled legs ending in block toes. *Parke-Bernet Galleries*

Below: Delicate carving and pierced work distinguish this Chippendale tea table from simpler versions of the same period. *Philip Colleck*

or fretwork, referred to as "Chinese railing," formed aprons on cabinets, backs of chairs and quite remarkably the legs, stretchers and galleries of tables. Chippendale's craftsmen found endless ways to incorporate bamboo, bells, dragons and birds into their Chinese designs, most of which were executed in mahogany, but some of which were of soft woods that bore rich, japanned finishes.

Although the Chinese taste was not strictly a part of the rococo style that English cabinetmakers borrowed from French ornamentalists, its occurrence at the same time is not surprising, since both did possess the same qualities of richness and fantasy. In fact, the English cabinetmakers appeared to understand the imaginative quality of Oriental inspiration better than the light, airy, asymmetrical designs that were being produced in Paris.

The rococo style was introduced in London by Matthias Lock, a carver and engraver who pioneered the look in the late 1740's. Both Lock and H. Copland, with whom Lock wrote *A New Book of Ornaments* in 1752, are believed to have worked for Chippendale in the 1750's and may well be responsible for the development of the rococo in their employer's workshop.

The rococo style is never as harmonious or as believable in England as it is in France. Great attention was paid to the motifs of the style, and less to the total shaping of sinuous silhouettes. Often the rococo was combined with Chinese or Gothic elements, diluting its effect further. The total impact is of enrichment without grace or fantasy. The rococo style is best seen in smaller furnishings—mirrors, brackets and candlestands—but larger designs also incorporate riotous ornament. There were Chippendale's riband-backed chairs, his scrolled or swan-necked pediments on secretary cabinets, his undulating foliage on china cabinets, his bombé fronts on chests and cabriole legs on chairs.

The Gothic style in Chippendale's hands is the most exotically carved of all, particularly in the chairs he produced. If the effect of the Gothic ornament makes these mid eighteenth-century designs seem more Gothic than those produced in the fifteenth and sixteenth centuries, it may well be because the ornament and not the basic silhouette was borrowed from the past, and was so exaggerated that it dominated the furnishings it embellished.

Among the most often-used motifs were the ogee arch to shape the tops of cabinets and the perpendicular tracery effects worked into bookcase façades as well as the pierced neo-Gothic details on chair backs. What is known of cabinetmakers of the time is that they possessed a general confusion as to what was Chinese, Gothic and rococo, a fact that accounts for the mixing and mingling of the ornamental details on furnishings. A chair, for instance, might have the Chinese silhouette, a pierced back borrowed from the Gothic idiom, and the suggestion of a scroll or tassels in the French taste carved into the frame.

The variety of chairs made by Chippendale and other cabinetmakers of the period began with those that had backs and sides of latticework panels, top rails with or without pagoda cresting, and bamboo or straight legs—all reflect-

Chippendale dining chair in the French taste is topped by a Cupid's-bow cresting rail, has a pierced splat and straight legs joined by an H stretcher. *Parke-Bernet Galleries*

Ladder-back, straight-legged chairs introduced for dining-room use like this George III mahogany design were plain or had pierced crest rail and matching splats and molded legs joined by H-form stretcher. *Parke-Bernet Galleries*

ing the Chinese taste. There were also ladder-back, straight-legged chairs introduced for dining-room use, like the armed version that sold recently for $675, and the set of ten side chairs that were $2,000. At the same time, a tall hooded porter's chair made after the period, and covered in a luxurious, buttoned maroon leather, studded with brass nailheads, brought $2,100. Obviously age does not always command the peak prices.

Then there were the neo-Gothic designs with splats pierced in ogee and tracery patterns. The rococo designs had riband backs on squared legs, or cartouche-shaped backs in the manner of Louis XV. These French chairs, as well as the all-upholstered bergères with their padded elbow rests, were supported by cabriole legs terminating in either claw-and-ball or whorl-end feet. All such chairs are rare today and sufficiently in demand to command moderate to high prices. Those of moderate quality can be found for $300 and up, but for fine work one must expect to pay in four figures.

Mention should be made of the writing chairs of the time. These popular designs in tub shape on tapered legs wearing spade toes, may cost as little as $325 in a fortunate find.

Sofas produced in the third quarter of the eighteenth century were more French than English, Chinese or Gothic in appearance. The rococo settee with its mahogany base ending in whorl feet, has scrolled arms, at the same height as the curvaceous back. Some sofas, large enough to seat four, varied the design. Arms start at the back at the level of the top rail and slant downward slightly. The base is one continuous undulating line with four legs in front, four in back as supports. This type of sofa with restrained curves with cabriole legs, is one of the most satisfying of all produced with these multiple underpinnings either in England or on the Continent. Today, however, few period examples are available. When they are, prices rise from four to five figures.

Stools, whose eminently useful designs might be the simplest seating forms, are still among the most popular items and command high prices. Square seats, cabriole legs carved at the knees with bound foliage are the type of stools that command $1,000 or more. A pair sold recently for $2,750 and was considered an excellent buy.

Dining-room furnishings are almost entirely limited to tables—both those that were used for serving and those that were used for dining. The early gateleg-style table would be difficult to find today, but the oval- or circular-topped designs are more numerous. A sectional table standing on two pillars with tilting tops, each supported by four reeded and splayed legs on casters, cost $1,750 in 1968. But good ones can also be found for about $1,000.

The marble-topped sideboards also command impressive prices, from about $800 up. Their practicality in today's home both as sideboards, hall tables and in the living room, makes them ever in demand.

During the Chippendale period, some of the French dining habits were copied, and so were the furnishings that supported them. Like the French, who almost invariably disdained the great dining hall in favor of small salons, the English, perhaps less frequently, were happy to get rid of their servants so that they might entertain guests at small suppers in privacy. Thus were born the tripod-based dumbwaiters, those eminently practical, three-tiered tables revolving on a shaft. The trays on the tiers contained the food, plates and utensils—all that a host at a small repast required to satisfy his guests, whom he served or who served themselves.

Tea tables evolved into eminently desirable furnishings in this period. One

The English relied on their squat, square seats or stools to provide additional seating in the mid eighteenth-century home. These early George III stools are carved at the knees with foliage and stand on claw-and-ball feet with ringed collars above. *Parke-Bernet Galleries*

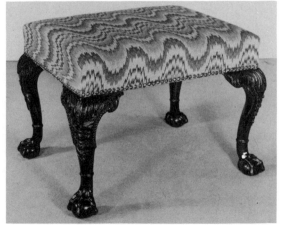

An early Chippendale wine table with lobed and dished top has a scalloped edge, birdcage top support and a tapered, fluted pillar base with tripod legs ending in hairy claw feet. *Parke-Bernet Galleries*

A large mahogany piecrust table measuring thirty-three inches in diameter is set on a tripod base ending in shapely snake-head feet. The Chippendale design dates from about 1760. *Philip Colleck*

of the most decorative types of tea table is the large tilt-top, circular table on a tripod base with a scalloped edge. The tilt-top made it possible for the table to be placed against the wall when not in use. Occasionally one sees tilt-top tables with dished or scooped fittings for plates standing on tripod bases. But piecrust designs are in greater abundance. A tilt-top table with scalloped edge set on a "birdcage"-topped column and ending in a tripod base recently sold for $800. Another one brought $1,100.

Smaller, round-topped tables were also popular—and still are today—serving as accessory or end tables in living rooms. A wine table of this type might cost $275 or more at auction. Oblong tables, especially those fragile designs in the Chinese taste with pierced gallery, legs and stretchers, which were called china tables in that period, and were used for serving tea, certainly are among the prettiest tables of all.

Tables from the Chippendale era, although plentiful, are prized by collectors and are not always available at auctions or in shops. When they are, the prices can often reflect their popularity. But patience and careful shopping can net some good buys like the pair of marble-topped designs that sold for $500 recently. One fine example of a Chinese Chippendale china table available recently in a New York shop carried a price tag of $6,500. But more modest examples can sometimes be found for from $1,000. For a good tilt-top table of the period one must expect to pay $2,000 or more.

Another rare and prized table is the supper table with drop leaves at either end of the oblong top, a drawer in the apron and a base framed on four sides with chicken wire. The straight-legged designs have caster feet. Prices will be in four or five figures for this choice furnishing.

The type of bedroom furnishings produced generally followed those popular in France in the same period. The toilet or dressing tables were of kneehole design with a top drawer concealing a mirror and compartments for combs and brushes. There was another kind with hinged lid opening out to either side and fitted with trays for toilet accessories. Both types of vanities, as they would be called today, are uncommon in the marketplace. The few examples that do come up for sale bring prices in four or five figures.

The washstands of the time had cabinet bases in which chamber pots were kept. Most are rather utilitarian-looking furnishings. The few that are more elaborate bring moderate to high prices today. The same is true of the shaving or basin stands and the night tables. A small bedside cupboard with a serpentine front supported by bracket feet cost $225 recently, a low price that can be partly explained by the fact that the two-drawer base had been changed to one deep drawer. Alterations in antiques, even if the change makes the furnishing more usable, invariably lower the price.

Clothes cupboards, at least in their surface decoration, looked as French as the armoires produced in Paris. But the shaping is squared, never curved as in those made for the châteaus of the Loire region. Commodes made by some of Chippendale's contemporaries like John Cobb go one step further, assuming a late rococo silhouette and inlaid with marquetry patterns of rare delicacy and refinement. Cobb, with his partner William Vile, served as cabinetmakers to George III and Queen Caroline and were among many of Chippendale's colleagues who fashioned superb designs for England's aristocracy and upper middle classes.

Chippendale called anything a commode that had a drawer in it and was used for storage. One of the most beautiful examples of this producer's commodes is in the Chinese taste. The black and gold rectangular silhouette, pierced gallery on three sides, lacquered scenes and motifs on the three center drawers and the two flanking cupboards, and the japanned squared legs show the exquisite detailing that Chippendale's artisans did so masterfully.

A George III chest of drawers for bedroom use might have a serpentine or bowed front, brass rings for pulls on the four graduated drawers, and a base of bracket feet. One may expect to pay about $850 or more for such a design. One in the Chinese taste with ormolu handles, and a serpentine front on bracket feet was $1,550 in a recent sale.

As for beds, little that is distinctive survives outside major collections and museums. But the pagoda-topped carved wood design that Chippendale made for Badminton, the seat of the Duke of Beaufort in England, is one of the most exquisite and exotic designs ever devised for sleeping. The deep-red lacquered bedposts touched with gilding, the pierced fretwork covering the high headboard, the pale green gilt and red roof show the hands of master cabinetmakers.

The small step stool made by Chippendale and his contemporaries for bed-side use sometimes contained a space inside for a chamber pot. These designs are now used for everything but for what they were intended; actually the step stool is most popular today as a planter.

Bookcases abounded in mid to late eighteenth-century England, and their popularity is shown in the large number of designs Chippendale offers in the third edition of the *Director*. It is assumed, however, that the fourteen elaborate examples given in the book were modified considerably when produced. Book-cases and secretaries show the last vestiges of the Palladian architectural mode. The breakfront design, surmounted by pediments in scroll design were, how-ever, combined with elements of other styles.

The pierced Gothic or Chinese fretwork in the scroll or swan-neck pediment

Right: Rent tables of late eighteenth-century England were made for work, thus ex-plaining the heavier propor-tions than was usual in living room furniture of the period. This circular, drum-topped design with tooled leather stands on a cupboard base. *Parke-Bernet Galleries*

Left: This burled yewwood writing desk of kneehole de-sign is from the third quarter of the eighteenth century. The rococo details—ormolu handles, the modified serpen-tine front, the bowed center drawer and the shaped bracket feet—are unusual in George III designs. *Parke-Bernet Galleries*

and the rococo serpentine front occur regularly. Both bookcases and secretaries are hard to find today and command moderate to high prices depending on quality and where they are found. One may expect to pay from $1,000 up for secretaries and bookcases. In recent seasons bookcases have brought between $1,000 and $3,000. A small one at one auction cost $2,000, but a more modest, though larger, mahogany design, measuring seven feet eight inches high and five feet wide, cost a surprisingly low $1,100; and a larger one seven and a half feet long cost $3,000.

Probably one of the most prized furnishings of all today are the library steps made in this period as combination table-ladders. The design is so simple— oblong in shape, squared legs, caster feet and rodlike rails for the upper stairs of the spare ladder—that a modern designer two centuries later would be hard put to improve on its simplicity. Prices on such library ladders reflect not only the fine design but also today's great interest in books. They run from four figures up to five figures.

Period partners' desks of the time were mammoth furnishings of a scale required for use in offices by from two to four persons. One such outsized design in elephantine proportions was made in 1760 and has a kneehole cut into each of its four sides, a simple façade and drawers in the apron. There are also drawers flanking the kneeholes and small cupboards behind doors at either end of each of the two long sides. One for two partners, its top covered with tooled maroon leather, contains three drawers in the frieze on each side, as well as drawers and cupboards on either side of the kneehole openings. It cost $750.

But other desks of the time had serpentine fronts for the drawers that flanked the kneehole opening. Such designs are available from time to time for about $750 and up, as a recent sale at Parke-Bernet indicated. The writing tables made for the libraries of Chippendale's wealthy clients were far more ornate. Lions, an Italian Renaissance favorite in ornamental detail, surmounted the tapered pillars at the four corners and flanking the kneehole. Each lion had a brass ring in his mouth, shaped to match the brass handles on the drawers. Gadrooning is a second Renaissance characteristic of this mahogany design. Chippendale writing tables with serpentine silhouettes, corners carved with cabochons and foliage, and its drawers fitted with ormolu handles, bring about $3,500, as was shown at a recent sale.

Desks were such weighty designs in their time that it is assumed that many were destroyed, as fashions for lighter-scaled designs became more important toward the end of the eighteenth century, or when the buildings these desks were designed for were eventually destroyed.

ADAM

After George III became king in 1760, the eclectic styles that had typified the work of Chippendale and other cabinetmakers began to decline in importance. Chippendale recognized the change and became active around 1770 in neoclassic furniture production. But the genius of the third quarter of the eighteenth century was not Chippendale but the architect Robert Adam, an eighteenth-century man with a sixteenth-century appetite for art.

The architect Robert Adam brought a new idea to England after four years of travel and study in Italy. Born in 1728, the son of an architect, Adam trained as an architect in his father's office after completing his studies at Edinburgh University. In 1754 he went to Italy where for the next several years he steeped himself in the culture of classicism, emerging from his studies with the firm intention of designing everything in a house from the building itself down to the last doorknob. But, as time would show, the architect was most often considered a man to refurbish the interiors of houses rather than to design new homes. It is on these renovations that his fame rests.

While in Italy, Adam met Piranesi, the engraver and architect. Giovanni Battista Piranesi became the single strongest influence on Adam, an influence that would leave its classical mark on interiors—floors, walls, ceilings and furnishings made over the next thirty years. During Adam's stay in Italy the excavations at Herculaneum, begun in 1738, were well under way. The diggings at Pompeii would commence in 1763. Neoclassicism took a deep hold on his mind, and following his return to London, he became the most exacting classicist of the late eighteenth-century decorative arts.

The switch back to classicism did not occur overnight, as nothing ever does in furniture design. First, classical ornament was applied to existing rococo designs, and such transitional combinations as the continued use of the cabriole leg on a commode bearing classically oriented winged griffins were the awesome and amusing result. Another change is the reshaping of the Chippendale splat on the backs of chairs into a lyre form.

But by 1762 the neoclassic style had taken root. Among the strongest elements of Adam furniture are the oval or lyre-shaped chair backs, the rams or female-headed capitols, the winged sphinxes and griffin finials, the honeysuckle (anthemion) borders, the vase and foliage swags, the husk festoons and urn bases.

Adam is said to have been responsible for more designs in furniture than any other architect before or since. He is credited with the development of the sideboard as it is known today. His influence was pervasive in his time and for several decades in England and America after his death in 1792. That his development of neoclassicism reached its peak before the Louis XVI style, also indicates that his designs evolved independently and not in the shadow of the French court.

A semi-elliptical extremely rare table with a top painted after a design by Michael-angelo Pergolesi stands on round, tapered and fluted giltwood legs topped by oval paterae. The Adam design is a distinguished example of the classic taste. *Parke-Bernet Galleries*

But the furniture specifically identified as Adam is far more difficult to find at auctions and in shops than that produced by his predecessors, contemporaries and followers. Perhaps this is true because the most notable Adam designs were the sideboards, cabinets, bookcases and side tables that were architectural in concept and designed for specific rooms in specific houses. Many still stand in the same houses or have been removed with the walls and ceilings around them to museums. A second reason is that actually some of his finest designs were grandiose in scale, an attribute which discourages moving them or collecting them for today's home. But the interpretations of Adam furniture with the exquisite detailing and spidery delicacy of ornament, toned down in the hands of lesser cabinetmakers, produced designs that were far more acceptable to the general public. And these furnishings carry other names.

Above: Adam giltwood console made around 1775 is richly carved with foliate details; its legs are topped by Ionic capitals; its frieze bears the fine chiseling of foliate and beaded motifs. *Philip Colleck*

Right: Adam carved mahogany armchair has a curved oval back framed in channeling, boldly shaped and padded armrests, round, tapered and fluted legs. The chair, shown here with old *grospoint* and *petit-point* covering, dates from the last quarter of the eighteenth century. *Parke-Bernet Galleries*

Then there was the matter of the way Adam worked. Often his designs are referred to as "by the Adam brothers." Two of Robert's brothers, James and William, worked at times with him, but James remained longer. However, as far as can now be determined the designing was done by Robert Adam and not the other members of his family. Adam also cooperated with Chippendale and lesser cabinetmakers. Records do not always show which one was the actual creator of many pieces, and indeed some of these collaborative efforts have resulted in designations of Adam-Chippendale and Adam-Hepplewhite.

The furnishings that do appear at sales and in shops show a wide range of prices. A pair of painted white and green armchairs with pierced backs centered by vase-shaped splats and framed by carved festoons of foliage sold for $450 in 1968. At a later sale a pair of upholstered, oval-backed side chairs with delicately outcurving legs sold for $1,600 the pair. A pair of mahogany side tables sighted recently were $1,600, and a slightly smaller painted pair in terra-cotta and black were $700. A bowfront commode, decorated with Grecian key fret and trellis borders, and showing a god driving a classical chariot, carried a surprisingly low $1,000 price tag.

HEPPLEWHITE

George Hepplewhite's name is better known to the average layman than is that of Robert Adam. Yet Hepplewhite contributed few, if any, original ideas to the evolution of cabinetmaking, nor did he claim to be an innovator. But he is credited with popularizing satinwood in furniture after 1765, about five years after he was known to have been at work in London. This wood continued in favor into the first quarter of the nineteenth century. Hepplewhite is also said to have commenced using painted motifs to embellish furniture surfaces and to have been the first to use the three-feathers motif, the emblem of the Prince of Wales, for a chair back.

Hepplewhite's furniture is not generally regarded as of the finest quality in late eighteenth-century cabinetmaking, and little if any of what he made for his modest clientele is believed to have survived. His use of soft woods for the carcasses of furniture, to which he applied fine veneers or paint, resulted in a less than sturdy product. The workmanship could not compare with the fine-quality designs that emanated from Chippendale's workshops, for instance; and the actual slender proportions of the Hepplewhite pieces, although elegant, graceful and extremely appealing, proved less than durable.

But Hepplewhite's work both in the furniture he produced and the designs he sketched for *The Cabinet-maker and Upholsterer's Guide*, published in 1788, two years after his death, had a strong influence on other cabinetmakers' work. As an interpreter of Adam and French designs Hepplewhite produced some interesting composites—cabriole legs on otherwise straight-line tables and settees. Such settees in the French taste, although not available in abundance, can still be found on occasion for around $800.

A typical 1780's Hepplewhite chair, for instance, has an oval back, curved and tapering arms and cabriole legs on whorl feet in the French style. An Adam chair had an oval back, the same curved arms and straight tapering front legs. The Adam design is purer and stronger, if less graceful, than the Hepplewhite design. Both have their devotees. Simple versions of Hepplewhite chairs are available at from $200 and up. Even better buys can be made if the designs are

Hepplewhite shield-backed chair, circa 1780, one of the most popular chair forms of the late eighteenth century, is delicately carved and painted with leaves and flowers in white and gold. The arms are serpentine, the rear legs angled and canted, the seat swelling forward at the front. *Philip Colleck*

of country origin, as were a set of eight that sold recently for $400. A finer set of six shield-backed chairs were sold for $525.

Hepplewhite's designs changed with the fashions. His characteristic, if not original, oval, heart and shield-shaped chair backs, had, by the late 1780's, squared, straight and tapering legs that bore a stronger note of kinship with the French Louis XVI designs than to the heavier classical silhouettes of Adam chairs.

Hepplewhite's Pembroke tables, as shown in the *Guide*, had square or oval tops. They were executed in satinwood and bordered with marquetry or painted decoration. The legs were squared and tapering, ending in small brass casters. These drop-leaf tables with hinged wooden brackets supporting the leaves and a drawer in the apron were used for dining throughout this period. Prices for these tables range from about $325 up.

Storage furnishings became increasingly important in the late eighteenth century. The bookcases, secretary cabinets, chests of drawers, clothes closets (or clothespresses, as they were called) and sideboards became plentiful as the burgeoning middle classes became ever more affluent. Designers like Hepplewhite, and those cabinetmakers who depended on Hepplewhite's *Guide* in the designs they produced, favored uncarved surfaces that were made highly decorative by the clever use of contrasting veneers. Mahogany banded by satinwood, or combinations of harewood and satinwood, were among the most favored. Such was the character of a chest-on-chest with a molded cornice and bracket feet, that sold in 1969 for $350.

The hallmarks of Hepplewhite's classically simple bookcases are the glazed metal bars fashioned into classical urns festooned with drapery or geometric patterns, a corniced top sometimes again surmounted by the much favored urn and flanked by scrolled foliage. The bases were of bracket feet or platforms. A particularly fine mahogany version measuring eight feet long and seven feet eight inches high was sold in New York City recently for $2,200. A smaller painted one sold for $550.

Secretaries and desks show some of the same characteristics as bookcases— the rectangular form, the pediment top, the festooning and scrolled decoration, the glazing bars on the doors of the upper cabinet all appear on the secretaries. The tambour desks are elegant designs standing on tall, squared and tapering legs with castered feet and, generally, with two drawers in the apron.

Chests of drawers most frequently were made with serpentine fronts containing two short and two long drawers supported by splayed feet joined by a shaped apron. Today such chests cost about $350 or more.

The sideboard came into its own in this period. The variations in the design and size of sideboards seems unlimited. Fronts were straight, bowed, serpentine and measured from five to nine feet in length. They were made fitted only with drawers or with drawers and cupboards. What the sideboard did in this period was to combine the smaller dining storage pieces that Adam had planned for

The Hepplewhite style embraced the French stylistic forms, as on this 1780 serpentine commode that emulates the rococo style then on the wane in Paris. The marquetry inlay of vases of flowers is bolder than French examples, showing strong individualism in the cabinetmaker. Satinwood and rosewood are the main woods used. *Philip Colleck*

A Georgian pine breakfront, probably built for a fine country manor and as part of an entire room, is distinguished by its simplicity. *Philip Colleck*

dining-room use. The sideboard and the cellaret were combined in one piece, for instance. The rash of storage pieces for the dining room was impressive not only in England but also in America. Further reference to this phenomenon is made in the separate section devoted to Hepplewhite in the chapter on American eighteenth-century furniture.

SHERATON

Thomas Sheraton, the author of *The Cabinet-Maker and Upholsterer's Drawing Book*, was even more influential than Hepplewhite on the furniture produced between 1790 and 1800 in England and up to 1820 in America. Again his fame and influence rest mostly on his *Drawing Book*, published in four parts between 1791 and 1794. More than six hundred cabinetmakers purchased the works in England alone, and in America both the *Drawing Book* and the many copies by others were widely known and used.

Right: In this Sheraton console, the round, fluted and tapered legs, the drapery festoons carved on the apron, the pendant palmettes at the capitals, show the neoclassic style. *Parke-Bernet Galleries*

Below left: Sheraton armchair with reeded arms, uprights and stick splats that are carved at the capitals with foliage. *Parke-Bernet Galleries*

Below right: Sheraton armchair, circa 1800, has molded uprights, ring-turned round and tapering legs with square seats rounded at the corners. *Parke-Bernet Galleries*

At no time, as is now known, did Thomas Sheraton even operate a cabinet-maker's shop. At his death at the age of fifty-five in 1806, his obituary, published in *The Gentleman's Magazine* noted that he had supported himself and his family since 1793 as an author. The second influential book of Sheraton's, *Designs for Household Furniture*, was published posthumously in 1812.

It is through the pages of Sheraton's *Drawing Book* that we see the work of other cabinetmakers. Not the least of these was Henry Holland, the architect, who had redecorated Carlton House, the Prince of Wales's home, in 1783.

Holland's work in stripping the interiors of buildings of the elaborate classical elements so favored by Adam and his followers brought English cabinetmakers closer to the chaste ideal now favored in architecture and interior design.

One device used by Holland in imitation of the Louis XVI style that delighted the English aristocracy of the day was the use of columnar elements on the corners of writing cabinets, cupboards and as leg supports. This characteristic is in turn fully exploited in the patterns offered by Sheraton.

As with Hepplewhite, Sheraton made much of painted furniture in his writings and designs. Often the façades of cupboards were to be decorated with oval medallions showing classical motifs or figural decorations. The columns were painted in contrasting colors to emphasize the fluted carving.

But in contrast to Hepplewhite, Sheraton's chairs are devoid of the softening influence of the heart, shield and curved back elements. Sheraton's chairs are almost without exception rectilinear designs. Splats comprise pairs of columns centered by a delicately worked urn that is framed by an elongated heart. Another chair back is the pencil-thin lyre motif or drapery swags surmounting a diamond-shaped medallion. Painted designs are invariably floral in character on these Sheraton chairs. And from this practice came the painted "fancy" chairs so popular in America in the early nineteenth century, and eventually the heavier Hitchcock chairs with their bolder and cruder decoration. The English Sheraton chairs can be found for about $200 and up. A set of six with squared backs fashioned into three reeded columnar splats sold recently for $900.

Also popular were the multiple seating designs like the painted three-chair-back settees, with each back pierced and decorated with columns and spears like one that sold for $325.

The oval medallion dominating the center of this corner cabinet is an ever-recurring theme in neoclassic English furniture of the Sheraton period. This satinwood design with serpentine front is also inlaid with urns, swags, bow-knotted drapery, classical figures and oak leaves. The Siena marble top and gilt metal feet are in harmony. *Parke-Bernet Galleries*

Sheraton hunt board, circa 1790, is prized today by collectors. The turned legs and castered feet on this mahogany design are hallmarks of the style. *Philip Colleck*

The chairs and settees that Sheraton designed in the French manner appear heavier and more straightforward than those produced in Paris. Settees can still be found for under $1,000, but not without patience and hard looking. However, the commodes and corner cabinets in this era captured the elegance and lightness of the French designs. A satinwood and mahogany commode in the French manner recently sold for $950, and a charming corner cabinet went for $750.

The small specialized tables of this period follow almost exactly the proportions and elegance of their French models. Most of these small tables were supposed to serve more than a single purpose—for writing or sewing. But by today's standards these delicate designs would be considered more decorative than useful, making them candidates for end tables.

The variety of small table designs include sewing tables standing on tall, squared and tapering legs, game tables set on trestle supports that are splayed at the base, oval worktables with a galleried top, and stretcher-like lower shelf between lyre supports—all embellished in one or more of a variety of ways: with marquetry, marble, painted designs or contrasting veneers. Game tables range from about $500, occasional tables from about $300, combination writing and dressing tables from about $550.

Library furnishings were as important to Sheraton as to Hepplewhite, and except in cases of extremely fine examples are about the same prices. Sheraton continued to favor the glazing bars on the upper doors of bookcases and secretaries but the patterns are curvaceous rather than angular or classical. Another

The "gothick" glazed doors, the molded cornice, the fall-front writing drawer and the cupboard in the base are hallmarks of the Sheraton secretaire-bookcase, here shown in mahogany. *Parke-Bernet Galleries*

Satinwood, which commands increased attention and rising prices in today's market, is the wood of this secretary made in the Sheraton style about 1780. The round pillars framing the base, the drop front of the writing surface, and the arched center section in the upper book cabinet are hallmarks of the neoclassic mode. *Philip Colleck*

point of difference is, of course, the inevitable columns at the front edges of the cabinets. Frequently there is a fan-shaped pediment surmounting the top.

Desks, or bureau cabinets as they were called, were made not only of mahogany or satinwood, but also of more exotic woods like rosewood. Sometimes, as in the case of a bureau cabinet sold in 1968 at Parke-Bernet, the upper part is in a breakfront form and is surmounted by a molded cornice. The interior reflected the masterly hand of late eighteenth-century, early nineteenth-century English cambinetmaking in its choice fittings. This one commanded the moderate price of $950. Less choice designs can still occasionally be found at more modest prices.

THE NINETEENTH CENTURY
Empire through Art Nouveau

Many parallels could be drawn between Napoleon and Louis XIV as far as the decorative arts are concerned. The roles they played in shaping art styles fully reflected what they considered their roles in history to be. Napoleon, like the Sun King before him, possessed an exalted view of himself, projecting his image as that of a Caesar or an Alexander. And like the seventeenth-century ruler, Napoleon cultivated the arts as the external expression of this view, so that there would be a full public appreciation of his imperial glory.

The Empire style commences with the proclamation of Napoleon as emperor in 1804, and ends about 1830. The Little Corporal, in one of his initial acts for the First Empire, appointed Jacques Louis David as court painter and art director, a role that Le Brun had played under Louis XIV. The classical orientation of David matched Napoleon's views, even if the emperor's conceits restrained the artist somewhat in the execution of the classical mode as he saw it should be expressed in art. David's first inclinations were for Spartan simplicity. Napoleon's were for all the trappings of pomp and circumstance that could be devised.

But unlike the age of Louis XIV, Napoleon's era was one in which the machine played a part. However slowly, mechanization in the production of furnishings had begun to reap a bounty for the middle classes, bringing them goods they could both afford and would find appropriate in their homes. In the seventeenth century, by contrast, the middle class did not exist as either a political or economic force.

The Empire style reached its zenith about the time that Napoleon returned from Elba in March, 1815. Thereafter began the slow decline, ending not with Waterloo in 1815, but with the July Revolution of 1830. The demise of the Empire mode is credited not to the decline of the emperor, but to the influence of the Industrial Revolution.

The Empire style spread beyond the borders of France to Austria following the marriage of Napoleon to the Austrian Princess Marie Louise. Later, Austrians and Germans called the style developed in Central Europe, Biedermeier. Through the Bernadottes, Empire reached Sweden. Through Napoleon's sister Pauline, it influenced Italy. Through Joseph Bonaparte, its mark was left on Spain. And because of its proximity to France, England adapted much of the Empire mode in its Regency style.

Unlike the beginning of neoclassicism under Louis XV, the Empire period no longer rescaled ancient models in fashioning furniture forms suitable to nineteenth-century living. Invention, which had been the trademark of the Directoire cabinetmakers, including Jacob, his son, Jacob-Desmalter, Rascalon, Burette and Lignereaux, was out. Antique was in. The public demanded true re-creations of the ancient designs. Needless to say, the wood furniture of Greece and Rome had not survived the volcanic burial but the metal furniture had. These designs, supplemented by those shown in paintings and reliefs on vases and sculptures, became the models for cabinetmakers.

The architects Percier and Fontaine insisted that furniture hie closer to the earlier forms and indeed look as if it had been designed for Julius Caesar. It was this team that remodeled the interiors of the Louvre, Versailles, Compiègne, Fontainebleau and Malmaison (the last for Josephine, Napoleon's first wife.) These architects and others went further in their reinterpretation of the past. Where models of furniture types did not exist, they created what they considered consistent with the ancient designs.

The delicacy in carving, the light scale, the simplicity of the Louis XVI designs would soon disappear under the severe and weighty silhouettes, the monolithic proportions, the solid unmolded paneling on the façades and sides of furniture and the sharply incised corners. Empire is a masculine mode, closer to Rennaissance than the feminine, eminently graceful, neoclassic eighteenth-century French furniture.

Mahogany commanded the scene almost exclusively in this period. It was cut and carved into furniture with heavy Tuscan and Doric columns and capitals both as pedestal bases for tables and as frames or stiles for chests, commodes, desks and secretaries. These columnar supports are never softened by chamfering the edges.

Baluster legs all but disappeared in this period, giving way to straight turned and squared legs. Block bases emphasize the monumental feeling of tables, bureaus and consoles. Surface carving is almost erased from the façades of furniture, except, perhaps for the occasional chair. Instead, ormolu mounts increase in number, once again serving as a natural contrast to the rich play of wood. But unlike earlier uses of ormolu, many Empire cabinetmakers lavished too many *bronze doré* mounts on their designs, all but obscuring the veneers. Symmetry, which had returned with neoclassicism, is followed rigidly.

There are very few innovations in furniture forms throughout the Empire period. Concentration on detailing and reshaping the great variety of chairs led to the creation of markedly different-looking designs. Even chairs were dressed up with metal mounts. Fauteuils have flared top rails ending in volutes. They were lightly padded and most often were not nearly so comfortable as those generously upholstered rococo and neoclassic designs of the earlier epochs. Chair seats retain slightly rounded fronts. Rear legs cant backward and front legs are cut straight and topped by animalistic arm supports, terminating in paw feet.

The animal forms that are distinctly Empire in character include winged sphinxes and lions, chimeras, eagles and swans. Another typical Empire motif

Empire bergères with roll-over top rails, arms supported by carved swans, gilded bronze appliqués on seat rails. Legs and cresting rail are supported on slightly curved legs. *Parke-Bernet Galleries (Taylor and Dull photo)*

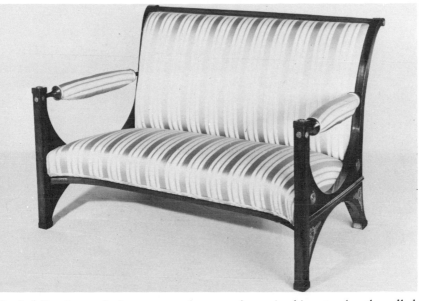

The classical Empire mode in an unusual cast as shown in this settee has the rolled crest rail and square front legs, but the armrests are upholstered poles and the pole crest rail joins over-scrolled uprights. Gilded bronze appliqués and paterae decorate the front and sides. *Parke-Bernet Galleries*

is the shell or palm leaf appearing on the stile directly above the joint that secures the arm to the back.

Tublike forms, reminiscent of Roman thrones, cradle the sitter in a lightly padded, wood-framed design. X-form and curule-type stools abound, continuing to serve the French as they had since the medieval period as the most popular form of seating.

Prices for Empire furnishings, in spite of the revival of interest in the style over the last ten years, remain moderate. This is particularly true of chairs. Fauteuils may well be the most expensive, commanding often about $700 each. Side chairs, however, are often far less expensive. A pair of chairs recently sold for $325. A pair of bergères sold for $650. And four mahogany side chairs sold for $525.

Sofas and settees designed in the era look like enlarged chairs. The Empire short sofa, called the méridienne, has arms at different heights in scroll form and a shaped back panel. Daybeds continued to be made in abundance in several variations. There are the backless styles with arms at equal height or at unequal height. The same designs were also made with backs. At recent sales a pair of settees sold for $1,000, and a single one went for $325.

Empire boat beds, one of the few new forms in the period, were designed to be placed lengthwise against the wall. Viewed in silhouette from the side, they look like boats, and that is the way they were intended to be seen. For this reason they were most often placed in a draped alcove.

Tables both large enough for dining, and small enough to support a single

Female masks in the Egyptian taste surmount the three term-shaped legs and ormolu claw feet that form the terminations on this Empire mahogany center table. The circular top is of gray marble; the base is a concave-sided, triangular pedestal centered by an ormolu urn. *Parke-Bernet Galleries*

candle were round or octagonal in shape. Thick marble tops, pedestal or tripod bases and animal carvings appeared on these and on many occasional tables of medium size. The round tables were distinguished by their triangular plinth bases.

Among the few rectangular tables were the *bureau plat* desk, often large enough to dine twelve comfortably, and the toilet tables. These vanities had frequently the lyre-like, trestle supports joined by a round stretcher, and a drawer hidden in the apron frieze. Rectangular consoles were also made and given rectangular pedestal bases. Tables were either of acajou (mahogany) or rosewood, decorated with generous splashes of gilt bronze, or they were painted pale gray and decorated with flat carvings in darker colors or gilding to simulate the ormolu used on expensive pieces.

Prices, although generally moderate for tables, often rise into four figures if the workmanship is out of the ordinary. Recently a distinguished mahogany center table with round top, female masks in the Egyptian taste topping the legs and a triangular base, sold for $1,100. A more modest card table with folding top, its legs also topped with grotesques, sold for $275.

Another specialty of the period was the dumbwaiter, that portable multi-level rack used to transport tablewares, food or papers. One recent example sighted in New York City had three graduated tiers, the center one attached to a gilded bulbous column and the others on smaller supports. The price was a remarkably low $175.

Desks and secretaries of the period differ only stylistically from their prede-

Rectangular tables, although rare in the Empire period, did appear in desks and, as here, a card table. This fruitwood and ormolu game table with folding top, lined inside and fitted with candlestands, is decorated with gilded shells and a palmette medallion. The legs are fashioned like quivers of arrows and joined by an X-shaped stretcher. *Parke-Bernet Galleries*

cessors. The drop-front secretary continues, as does the *bureau plat* and the rolltop or cylinder desk. Commodes and bookcases abound. A *bureau plat* with tooled leather top embellished with ormolu laurel wreaths, griffins, and on the legs the helmeted head of Apollo, sold not long ago for $550. Similarly inexpensive purchases have been and can still be made in *bibliothèques* (book cabinets). One with tambour doors flanked by half-round colonnettes sold recently for $300. An even more modest one was $130. But a truly fine example would bring from $800 into four figures.

The decline in craftsmanship became particularly evident following the restoration of the Bourbons to power. Neither Louis XVIII, who ruled from 1814 to 1824, nor Charles X, who remained on the throne six short years, did anything to stem the tide of deterioration in craftsmanship. Nor did they, for that matter, bring new inspiration to the style that had flourished under Napoleon.

The relatively high standards of the Empire period among the best cabinetmakers marked the last great period of French cabinetmaking. In spite of the difficulties of the post-Revolutionary period, expert *ébénistes* were able to reach the same level of artisanship as their eighteenth-century predecessors. But there were fewer of these skilled furniture creators, and volume production of furniture for the middle classes became increasingly more important.

Slowly developing industrialization under Napoleon quickened in pace with his removal from the throne in 1814. Before the Empire period had run its course, the parade of imitative forms had begun its march, a march that would cover a larger geographical territory than even Napoleon envisioned in his conquest of Europe thirty years earlier.

Characteristics of the Louis XVIII and Charles X styles are the ponderous character of the forms and the coarsening of all detail. Mahogany was slowly

Empire *bibliothèque,* with the top frieze centered with a Medusa mask flanked by stylized foliage, the façade framed by term-shaped pilasters surmounted by Egyptian masks, the cupboard doors similarly decorated with ormolu mounts and the plinth base on bun feet, shows the rich play of neoclassic decoration of the early nineteenth century. *Parke-Bernet Galleries*

The lighter woods in favor after the Empire period appeared not only in Biedermeier furniture but also in France in the Charles X style. Here the Empire weighty silhouette is even more exaggerated, but the paler well-figured thuya-wood lightens the effect of the squared back, the boldly scrolled armrests and the corbel-shaped legs. *Parke-Bernet Galleries*

eclipsed by the popularity of other woods. Light-colored veneers began to appear, possibly influenced by the paler woods used in Biedermeier furniture in Austria and Germany. Ormolu decoration was replaced by the more economical use of inlaid woods—light woods in dark, or dark woods in light. The motifs favored in these inlaid embellishments were acanthus leaves, palmettes, rosettes, geometric designs or wire-thin bands.

Louis Philippe may have held the throne longer than Charles X following his rise to power at the end of the July Revolution, but he exerted little or no influence over the potpourri of styles that began with Gothic and included Renaissance, baroque, Empire, and, after 1840, rococo. It is with this style that Louis Philippe is associated, just as Queen Victoria was during a similar revival in England.

There is little to praise in this rococo revival. But the cabriole legs, the weighty silhouettes, the use of Sèvres plaques, dark, ebonized woods, carved

Louis-Philippe *bonheur du jour* shows the lavish use of ormolu, Japanese lacquer and the vast repertory of decorative motifs: waterfowl, rockwork, mountains, festooned and tasseled drapery, ribbon-bound arrows and foliate appliquées. The lady's desk in purple heart has a three-quarter ormolu gallery surmounting the superstructure. *Parke-Bernet Galleries*

ornaments and gilding are beginning to appeal to the same generation of collectors who are finding English and American Victorian of interest today. Few examples of the French middle nineteenth-century designs are available here, and what is available will command the same or possibly lower prices than Empire.

BIEDERMEIER

Biedermeier is the much-derided yet eminently appealing style that evolved between 1820 and 1850 in Austria and Germany. Two sources are apparent in Biedermeier—the French Empire and the German painted peasant furnishings. The name Biedermeier was not used until 1853, three years after the actual style had lost favor. It derives from a cartoon character by the name of Papa Biedermeier, a self-opinionated oaf who was forever expounding on a variety of subjects including the decorative arts. He epitomized to many the middle-class taste of the day, especially to those who read the *Fliegende Blätter*, a sophisticated humorous magazine of the day.

The term was applied to the quaint and comparatively inexpensive style that at its worst was a hodgepodge of all neoclassic styles and of the peasant work. At its best, Biedermeier was almost a pure interpretation of the Empire mode.

The quality of the designs produced varied from poor to excellent—as under Napoleon in France. Proportions were sometimes awkward, curves clumsy. On the positive side, the rectangular, eminently sturdy Biedermeier was a satisfying architectural mode. The wardrobes, secretaries, cabinets and bookcases were boxy, rectangular and imposing designs. By 1840, however, even these pieces began to succumb to curves, ornament and rococo scrollwork as the style declined.

Chairs and tables in the Biedermeier period are cut with curves. Table supports were lyre-shaped or melonlike pedestals. Chair legs were concave or saberlike. Tabletops were, like the Empire ones, more often round than rectangular. But exceptions in all pieces existed. Some chairs, for instance, had legs tapering and straight as ramrods, backs shaped in rectangles and centered by carved fleurs-de-lis or shell motifs.

Prices on chairs are still extremely low when found at auction, higher in antiques shops. The reason for the lower auction prices might well be that frequently the few Austrian or German furnishings in a sale are overshadowed by French or English furnishings. Recently, for instance, six Beidermeier fruitwood chairs brought $300. On another occasion a pair sold for $140, and a set of five chairs were $250. In antique shops chairs generally command $200 and up.

Tables and cabinets also reflect the depressed prices for this style. A table may be found for as little as $175, and early in 1969 a walnut secretary sold for $120. A late Biedermeier cabinet in satinwood and rosewood sold for $200 and a walnut pedestal cupboard went for $140.

One of the easiest ways of telling Biedermeier from other nineteenth-century neoclassic styles is by the woods employed. Farm and orchard woods, including apple, elm, pear, cherry and birch, were the most favored. Many were given light finishes, or, when more than one wood was employed, inlays were handled quite differently from those in France. Carving was disdained by the Austrians and Germans in this period, but pressed brass ornaments in imitation of ormolu were employed to dress up the façades of all pieces. Since the Biedermeier began when Empire was on the wane, there is a marked difference in the basic silhouettes of the Central European designs.

Painted decoration did appear on many Biedermeier pieces. The motifs were mostly from antiquity, and animal, floral or classical vase and urn shapes were common. Unlike the Empire, the Biedermeier designs had humorous associations, a fact that may well have sparked the cartoon representation of Papa Biedermeier.

REGENCY

The Regency period in England, like the Empire era in France, shows the strong revival of interest in classicism that permeated the decorative arts of the time. Technically the Regency style corresponds to the years of George IV's reign as regent, from 1811 to 1820, but in reality the style begins earlier, and some aspects continue into the 1830's.

The form that classicism took in this period differed markedly from that of Robert Adam and also from the late eighteenth-century designs shown by Hepplewhite and Sheraton in their trade catalogs. The new classicism is more robust. It merges three cultures: Greek, Roman and Egyptian. Its inspiration came from the eighteenth-century diggings at Pompeii. The vases and other wares unearthed from the ancient city showed bold silhouettes; a strong hand modeling of furniture was depicted on these fragmentary vestiges of antiquity.

The roots of the Regency can be seen in the furniture designed by Henry Holland that blended elements of the French Directoire and of the Greco-Roman styles. Holland's late eighteenth-century designs were shown in Sheraton's *The Cabinet Dictionary* of 1803. Grecian sofas and tables that had exaggerated scroll arms, curvilinear legs and Greek key friezes are among the designs illustrated.

Once again it was the firm intention of innumerable designers to reproduce line-for-line copies of the designs as they existed in antiquity and as they were painted on the wares found at Pompeii. A half century earlier, Adam had attempted to do the same, and in so doing created some delicately carved furnishings, remarkable for their fragility. Nothing of that character would be forthcoming in the Regency period.

The main characteristics of the Regency style are the Greek curves, honeysuckle motifs, klismos backs, animal and human forms used as table and cabinet supports, X-form bases on chairs and the increased use of gilt metal in hardware and other embellishments.

Chairs are certainly the most imaginative designs of the epoch. Designers exercised a free hand interpreting the past, a tendency designers have in all

Black lacquer English Regency Récamier sofa has a klismos back, exaggerated scroll arm and the weighty character so typical of this era. It dates from about 1815. *Richard V. Hare*

William and Mary state bed, bedecked at the molded cornice corners with ostrich plumes and covered with crimson velvet, is framed with octagonal oak corner posts terminating in bases carved with gilded cherubs seated on scrolls. This bed was made about 1685 for the London house of Sir Dudley North and later was in Glenham Hall, Suffolk. *Parke-Bernet Galleries*

The serpentine outline and bombé contour were treated as an unbroken façade on this commode. The drawer handles disappear lest they distract the eye from the lavish marquetry work in bold colors. Kingwood, tulipwood and purplewood are combined in the commode that is topped with a brecciated marble slab with molded border. From the collection of Madame Lucienne Fribourg. *Parke-Bernet Galleries*

This imposing set of Louis XVI seating designs, signed by Georges Jacob, is part of a suite that comprised not only the canapé and fauteuils shown but also a pair of bergères and six other fauteuils. Frames are gilded wood, seats are bowed in front, legs are tapering and fluted and there are pomegranate finials topping the canapé's back stiles. From the collection of Helena Rubinstein. *Parke-Bernet Galleries*

The brilliant effects created by eighteenth-century *ébénistes* in marquetry decoration is clearly shown in this choice Louis XV *table à la Bourgogne* (writing table). The bold, intricately worked spray of flowers and foliage is executed in natural and stained wood on a fruitwood ground in the façade and, when open, in the faces of the jack-in-the-box nest of drawers. *Parke-Bernet Galleries*

The acanthus leaves capping the corbel-corners, the sunflowers flanking the lion's mask ring-pull, the spirally molded and tapering legs on this Louis XVI small commode were the work of Georges Kintz. The tulipwood design has a white marble top. *Parke-Bernet Galleries*

Furniture in such exotic materials as this mother-of-pearl canapé, chair and center table, have existed in every period, but they are always rare finds. These designs, part of a suite made for the Duc de Montpensier and formerly in the collection of Helena Rubinstein, have modified Empire silhouettes as in the Charles X period, and fine ormolu mounts. They date from about 1835.
Parke-Bernet Galleries

Superb proportions and detailing from its cove-molded swan-neck to its claw-and-ball feet mark this as one of the finest Philadelphia Chippendale highboys known. Leaf scrolls through the frieze, shell carvings in the apron and at the knees, and bat-wing brasses distinguish the mahogany design. *Parke-Bernet Galleries*

periods under the protective mantle of reproducing historical styles appropriate to modern living.

The saber-legged chairs in the Greek taste were possibly the most typical of the Regency period, and among the most popular today. The backs were slightly curved as on klismoses. The seats were either caned or upholstered. A pair of these chairs with an ebonized finish sold not long ago for $175. But the recent upsurge of interest in these chairs has pressed prices to three and four times that amount. Fine examples have always sold in four figures.

Bamboo turnings wrought in wood, framed a large majority of Regency chairs. Bamboo is one of the many examples of the lingering Oriental influence that pervaded the decorative arts after more than a century of favor. The high arms on these and most chairs of the period were a hallmark of the "antique" styles, as were the bamboo-like, round and tapering legs, the caned seats and the caned demilune back panels.

A set of six painted chairs of this kind recently were sold at auction for $780, a modest price and one rarely met in shops or, for that matter, at public sales. Another set of six chairs at a slightly lower price ($720), included in the same sale, were of different styling. The ogival uprights framed backs that were decorated with spread wings and spherules. The apron bore carved stars as appliqués. The legs were round and tapering.

Music chairs were another in the long list of specialty seating designs so favored in this era. The lyre-form back, often with a twisted ropelike metal handle at the crest of the back rail, was combined with the cane seat and saber legs. Most were painted, as was the chair that sold late in 1968 for $130.

Bergères of this time often bore the exaggerated classical motifs that were widely favored. The grotesque masks, mythological birds, winged female monopodes and claw feet were often combined on a single piece, as they were on a pair of gilt wood chairs that sold early in 1969 for $525. Still another unusual combination on chairs that are generally labeled as George IV (late Regency or post-Regency) was the carved foliage, wheat sheaf and flower heads with the scrolled arms and the pierced brass panels on seat rails. A pair that was sold early in 1969 had once been exhibited at Brighton Pavilion, that architectural jewel of the period. The price mirrored the distinctive character of the chairs; it was $4,300 for the pair.

As for the X-form designs, the stool was certainly one of the most popular. Although they are not common today, such small seating conveniences can be found for about $325 and up. Typical hallmarks would be the molded border carved with rosettes and bell flowers, the entire frame painted white with specks of blue and terminating in four ball feet.

The revolving piano stool, on which late nineteenth- and early twentieth-century designs were modeled, came in this period with a small, low and shaped backrest. The seat was often covered in leather and the legs were round, tapered and fluted. Such a design today may, on rare occasions, be found for as little as $190.

Shaped and reeded supports distinguish this William IV chaise, a style being reexamined today as the Regency style in all its variations continues to gain ascendance. The chaise is painted white and touched with gilding. *Parke-Bernet Galleries*

Like the French, the English favored the Récamier-type sofa with its curvaceous arms and splayed feet. The frame was generally reeded and scrolled, and bore brass rosettes, and on its brass toecaps were casters. A design of this type sold not long ago for $525, a low price that would generally be hard to match, for most sell for closer to $1,000.

Tables and cabinets may have shown less of the imaginative aspects of the Regency, but today they command far higher prices than do the chairs. There are, of course, the simple worktables of the period. They were oblong on top, had octagonal pedestals and quadrilateral bases, and cost around $200. But even trays-on-stands command far more. A papier-mâché oval tray on a folding coffee table base, decorated with foliage and butterflies, was sold for $325 early in 1969. A small writing table with adjustable book stand measuring twenty-seven inches long, twenty-nine inches high, was $300.

Finer writing tables with tooled leather tops, friezes inlaid with brass stringing, trestle feet and casters are hard to find today. Sometimes altered versions are seen in shops and at sales. Recently a pair of altered tables, made from one larger table, sold for $700. Unaltered tables usually bring twice the price, or for $700 each up.

Sofa tables with D-shaped drop leaves at either end are frequently inlaid with boxwood stringing and brass lines, and have end supports. For these, one must expect to pay from $400 into four figures. Satinwood versions begin at $1,000. Consoles usually have marble tops, and often their animalistic front legs support a rosewood frieze. The price: from $700 up. Center tables cost

Satinwood sofa table with the typical Regency end supports incorporating spindles and splayed at the toes, which terminate in lion masks. The curvaceous stretcher, the scrolled details under the drop leaves and the crossbanding of tulipwood are other period characteristics. *Parke-Bernet Galleries*

less, about $500 or more. Most have pedestal bases, are decorated with ormolu appliqués and foliate borders and stand on scroll feet. They cost from $500 up.

The swivel-topped card tables were often made with canted corners and had leather-lined playing surfaces. The bases are of painted black pillars, touched with gilding. Four feet splay out from the pillars, ending in casters. One may expect to pay about $500 and more for such designs.

What were considered occasional tables, and today might serve as large end tables, generally have the trestle supports in lyre or reverse scroll form and are frequently of rosewood. These are decorative tables, glittering with inlaid or applied metal mounts and standing on brass casters. They cost $950 and up today. Plainer ones in black lacquer with circular tilting tops trimmed with red and gold chinoiserie decoration can sometimes be found for as little as $400.

Regency dwarf cabinets, of the size and proportions of Renaissance *credenzinas*, are, in many cases, wondrous designs. Gilt metal inlays center the rosewood doors. Gilt metal borders frame the oblong tops. Gilt metal grotesque masks top the stiles, and gilded claw feet form the base supports. Such cabinets, measuring about thirty-seven inches high and forty-four inches long, brought $2,200 in 1968 at Parke-Bernet.

But there are plainer, more economical buys in Regency cabinets. A maple wood design, slightly smaller than the typical dwarf cabinet, recently sold for $225. Those with chinoiserie decoration, finished in black lacquer and decorated with gold in the Chinese taste, cost about $700 and up.

It is often in the unusual examples of a period that the prices rise to extraordi-

Rare revolving bookcase made in England in the early nineteenth century has *trompe-l'oeil* shelf supports looking like books on the five top graduated tiers. The mahogany design is inlaid with ebony, has lion-mask ring handles on the lower section, and stands on claw feet. *Parke-Bernet Galleries*

nary heights. Recently a decorated Canterbury, a portable rack for plates, cutlery and trays, with a gilt metal handle on the top and embellished with classical motifs, was sold at auction for $1,500. And a camp bed in the Egyptian taste that would serve as a chaise in a contemporary bedroom brought $2,100.

Library furnishings, the pride of the eighteenth and nineteenth centuries in England, are not found easily, but they can be prizes when located. The revolving bookcase might well prove to be a buy, since today's library is so much better contained in floor-to-ceiling shelves that the small bookcase seems totally inadequate. Prices, though, are bound to be in four figures. The same would be true of the library ladder, the folding elephant ladder brought back from India and usually decorated with leather and brass nailheads. Prices begin at $1,000. However, a simpler ladder concealed in the base of a cane chair, recently sold at auction for a more modest figure—$250.

THONET

The Victorian era produced one of the greatest furniture designers of all time. Michael Thonet (1796–1871) was the son of a humble cabinetmaker of

Boppard in the Rhineland. He was trained as a craftsman, and by the time he was twenty-three years old, was consumed with the idea that chairs could be made lighter, more durable and less expensive than ever before.

Thonet began extensive experiments that led him in 1836 to produce the first laminated veneer chair—or what we would call today the first plywood chair. This "technological explosion," as Henry Dreyfuss, the industrial designer, calls the development, did not at first change the appearance of furniture.

There are obvious roots of the French Empire, German Biedermeier and American Federal styles visible in Thonet's first chair. Even the chair's extraordinary hairpin legs, looped bundles of veneer that had been saturated with glue and bent under heat in molds, are more interesting technically than as original design.

Following Thonet's move from South Germany to Austria in 1842 came more experiments with heating and steaming wood to make it more pliable. Later, he molded furniture parts under pressure. In 1850 Thonet made the first chair framed with solid rods of bentwood. Thonet understood the exuberant spirit of the Victorian age, as can be readily seen in the pair of upside-down G-clefs that form the curlicued back of the 1850 Café Daum chair. Although framed in bentwood, the seat of this chair is still conventionally covered with fabric or petit point.

Cane seats and backs were, however, beginning to be introduced at this time. Thonet's armchair, side chair, settee and table shown the following year at the spectacular Crystal Palace Exhibition in London were similarly caned.

It is the Vienna chair of 1859 that fully characterizes the whole spirit of Michael Thonet and his five sons for whom the father created the concern of Gebruder Thonet. The chair is simplicity itself, a rhythmic series of bentwood loops framing a laminated wood seat. The Vienna chair was conceived as a low-cost design for mass production and became the most sat-on chair in the world. This distinction probably still holds true today more than one hundred years after its creation. The importance of the chair cannot be overestimated. Its interchangeable, standardized parts were shipped knocked-down to all parts of the world, where they were assembled quickly and cheaply, in much the same way that cars and their parts used to be exported.

No wonder that by World War II, an estimated fifty million Vienna chairs, also called café chairs, had been produced and shipped from Thonet factories. Possibly another fifty million were made and sold by Thonet's competitors after the original patents ran out in 1869.

Until a few years ago such chairs, originals or copies, could be found for 50 cents or a few dollars. But since the early 1950's, when the revival of interest in bentwood began, prices have soared. And, it must be noted, originals and copies are still being produced of the original designs but in varying degrees of quality. Production of these designs is centered in the United States, Germany, Yugoslavia, and Czechoslovakia, to mention the best-known sources.

Prices for old Thonet designs, ranging from the simple Vienna chair to the

Bent beechwood was favored by Gebruder Thonet, producers of the three designs shown here. The rocking chair with cane seat and back is a graceful study in curves and scrolls. The design dates from 1860. The armchair, still favored by modernists for homes and offices, is from 1870. The wood-seated side chair, circa 1876, is known as the Vienna Café Chair. Collection, the Museum of Modern Art, New York; gifts of Café Nicholson and Thonet Industries, Inc.

elaborately worked rocker of 1860, range from a few dollars to four figures. Some simple Thonet chairs produced in the nineteenth century can still be found for $25 and $50 each. Shoppers should check the underside of the seat for the burned-in maker's name or metal plate, for it was the practice to identify the factory of both Thonet and his imitators.

Rockers are becoming very rare in antiques shops. Usually they command several hundred dollars into four figures. Children's high chairs, mostly of late vintage and by copyists, have been purchased for as little as $35 and up. And there are the extremely rare and more costly cradles, the coat racks (low in price at $200 to $300), settees, beds, dressing tables, dining tables, student chair-desks, rocking chaises, platform rockers and the three-legged shooting stick with the crook back. With the exception of the coat racks, these furnishings are difficult to locate, at least in original nineteenth-century versions, and prices will range from a few hundred to a few thousand dollars.

Most of Thonet's bentwood designs were produced in Carpathian beech, a close-grained wood that readily bends under heat and pressure into complex shapes without splintering. On occasion, special cuts of oak, elm and birch were also used. Most of the early designs were given dark, almost black finishes. But from the turn of the century onward, there were many blond wood designs made. Those with coats of paint have probably been so treated by recent owners and not by the original makers.

By 1953 there were two images of Thonet chairs. The most public view was the chair that was smashed on the head of the villain in the television Westerns, a cliché that thankfully has disappeared from video. But, at the same time, a coterie of Thonet collectors had begun to form. They snatched up pieces at such low prices (unless the seller was astute enough to know the value of what he had) that the escalation in price when reported today sounds phenomenal. In many cases prices have risen 1,000 per cent or more.

Just how modern Michael Thonet and his sons were was demonstrated in 1953 by the Museum of Modern Art in its Thonet exhibition. Possibly for the first time in America, the public was shown the mid nineteenth-century designs of the Thonets in a modern museum setting. American collectors suddenly discovered the style, mixing it with steel and glass designs of twentieth-century designers.

The late Greta Daniel of the museum, writing in the catalog of the Thonet exhibition, noted that by the first decade of the twentieth century, thirty-five thousand persons were employed in the bentwood industry. Such a figure should make bentwood collectors who travel abroad, take heart. It is well worth taking the time in distant cities for bentwood furniture. Even in Vienna, where Michael Thonet won fame a century ago, unbelievably inexpensive finds were made recently. John Sailor, a Viennese lawyer, went through his native city cleaning out attics and paying less than $5 in many cases for excellent examples of Thonet designs. The collection he gathered has been exhibited in two shows in this country in recent years, further publicizing the style. He and others believe there are similar finds to be made from Africa to Arkansas and at equally modest prices.

WILLIAM MORRIS

William Morris was still a household name to Americans in the 1920's and probably still is to most British subjects. But the assumption in this country had always been that Morris designed furniture. Most experts now believe that

Morris spearheaded the arts and crafts movement of the second half of the nineteenth century, but that he never designed any furniture at all. Even the Morris chair that bears his name was probably devised by someone in his employ. The upholstered seating design with an adjustable back bar was the forerunner in both purpose and popularity of today's recliners.

Morris, born in 1834, grew up in a period when the Gothic revival produced chairs in London living rooms that had pointed arched backs, tracery carving and boxy silhouettes. The elaborately carved tables exploited the motifs, if not the spirit, of the medieval period. More often than not, these neo-Gothic furnishings looked like caricatures of the originals.

Trained as an artist and architect, Morris was a follower of John Ruskin, the art critic and author, and shared the same love of the Gothic age. In the same period Charles Lock Eastlake also spoke of ridding furniture of embellishments, but he never went far enough. Both Morris and Eastlake were deeply imbued with a love of antiquity, but Morris was more successful in producing furniture of rugged simplicity than his colleague. His workshops for stained glass, wallpapers, textiles, accessories and furniture maintained high standards of craftsmanship. And in furniture the joinery techniques, materials and solidity came surprisingly close to the ideal he aspired to.

Although William Morris is praised for the new focus he placed upon the arts and crafts, he was as conservative in his thinking as Thonet was progressive. Disavowing the machine and the phenomenal technological improvements of his age, he persuaded artists and artisans to take up ancient tools in order to refashion furnishings in the spirit of the Middle Ages. He was, in fact, as romantic and as burdened with nineteenth-century æsthetics as were the revivalists who were putting Louis XV, Louis XVI, Renaissance and those Turkish furnishings in Victorian parlors. But as is always the way in the history of the decorative arts, the reevaluation of ancient craft techniques brought a parallel rethinking of the concepts of simplicity and functionalism. What we now call the modern design movement erupted out of a further evolution of these ideas, long before the Art Nouveau movement was nurtured into being.

Morris revived traditional farmhouse furniture. The Sussex chair with the rush seat and ebonized frame was updated then, as it would be again in the 1950's. Examples of this chair as made by Morris and Company probably exist abroad, but are rarely sighted in American shops. Interpretations made here are relatively inexpensive, ranging from $25 to $100.

By comparison, the upholstered Morris chair looks terribly dated today. The ratchet device making the chair adjustable and permitting the sitter to sit up straight, recline at a slight angle, or almost assume a sleeping position offered new comfort, an ideal devoutly sought as the nineteenth century drew to a close. American versions of this chair are more often found in charity bazaars than in antiques shops. Covered with plush or carpeting, versions recently sold cost from $40 to $100.

Philip Webb, Morris' designer, was responsible for many neo-Gothic furn-ishings. The oak trestle tables with castlelike motifs in their underpinnings were his designs. He also did large wardrobes framed with posts that were carved with the rope motif of the Gothic age. The doors and sides of these pieces were frequently painted by colleagues. Edward Burne-Jones painted one with scenes from Chaucer's "The Prioress's Tale," as a wedding present to Morris in 1858 or 1859.

The custom-designed Morris furniture, if it begins appearing at auctions or in shops, is bound to command high prices. The quality of workmanship was of the highest order in an age when standards of craftsmanship were at their lowest, and the artistic quality of the painted decoration adds to their intrinsic worth. Copies of these designs made in the period, however, will probably bring very little. Cupboards have been sold for as little as $150 and $200. Tables bring $100 or less.

EASTLAKE

Hard on the heels of the Renaissance revival in the 1860's came the so-called Eastlake style. This revival of rural and more formal designs from the Eliza-bethan through the Jacobean periods, became widely popular. Charles Lock Eastlake, the English architect, was a reformer who forcefully presented his ideas on taste in *Hints on Household Taste in Furniture, Upholstery and Other Details,* published in 1868. Unfortunately the furniture he later produced was far less meaningful than his book.

Eastlake, like Morris, called for a return to sturdy furniture. He stressed the importance of quality workmanship. With Morris and others, he took up the banner for sobriety, simplicity and a return to geometric forms as a reaction against the exuberance of the Victorian age. It is a credit to him and the teach-ings and writings of others that other furniture producers began to heed their words long before the twentieth century dawned.

Eastlake's square-cornered dressers, tall chests, cylinder, slant or fall-front secretaries, his bookcases and corner cupboards may have been considered dras-tically different in their day, but the differences are not as apparent today. That Eastlake was more interested in architectural-type furnishings, that he insisted on and obtained "honest," medieval-type craftsmanship (although American copies were often shoddily made), is apparent.

But Eastlake's furniture is more richly carved than the sixteenth- and seven-teenth-century originals on which they were based. Baluster-edged galleries surmounted secretaries, like the designs in enlarged form topping buildings of that era. Carved frames bore geometric motifs for the most part. But occasion-ally nonfunctional, scalloped bases, scrolls and finials appeared.

The outsized scale of many of the Eastlake designs would probably make these pieces less costly and on a par in price with the Renaissance revival de-signs. With the exception of the cylinder-front desk, a forerunner of the ubiquitous rolltop, the bureaus (meaning, in the American sense, chests of drawers), the bookcases, cupboards and the like will probably cost about $100 to $250. The cylinder-front desks will more than likely be from $300 to $600.

ART NOUVEAU

During the 1890's and the early decades of this century, designers, artists, architects and artisans throughout Europe and in America were shaping a fresh expression in the decorative arts that we now identify as Art Nouveau.

The innovators in Europe and here followed two different courses, but both depended upon the naturalistic trend in the embellishments of their furniture designs. Three architects who spearheaded one aspect of the movement were Charles Rennie Mackintosh, of Scotland; Josef Hoffman, of Austria; and Frank Lloyd Wright, of the United States. Square, austere silhouettes emerged in their furniture. There is a Gothic simplicity evident in their designs that with all his efforts William Morris never achieved. But the decoration of these "new style" furnishings depended upon the vocabulary of ornament of the period. Floral and foliate inlays, paintings and ironwork were used. Stained glass brightened the façades of some designs. And on the most severe designs of all, those by Wright, the latticework of wood strips and touches of glass or ceramic inlay show their indebtedness to the mode.

Little is known of the market value of these designs, for public sales have been few and private sales rarely divulge figures. But until a few years ago Mackintosh furniture went begging in London antiques shops and was even less well known in Glasgow where much of it had been made at the turn of the century. Now the fashion for Mackintosh is in full swing and it is doubtful that bargains can be found in either British city.

Wright's furniture, limited in production to the houses he designed and where most of his furniture still stands, is even more difficult to pinpoint. There are those who would pay from $200 to $500 for his curved-back chairs framed in sticklike wood. But none have been offered at public sale, to the best of expert knowledge.

But the architect-innovators are of lesser importance than the designers and European architects who freed the silhouette of their designs from the boxy strictures of the neo-Gothic and neo-Renaissance revival styles. Hector Guimard of France captured the curvilinear feeling and tight control of the graphics and the silver, Favrile glass and jewelry in some of the most impressive designs of the age. Guimard's style, readily identifiable because of the cast-iron, orchid-like stalks guarding the entrances to some of the Paris Métro stations, is a full-blown baroque spirit.

In the work of Guimard, Louis Majorelle and Emil Gallé one finds the strong echoes of the rococo and earlier French modes. A dining table and

Above right: Frank Lloyd Wright, in this pine armchair that he devised in 1904, proved the most austere of the group of architect-designers. The slab back and side panels, the squared stick legs and stretchers anticipate the post-World War I school of thinking. Collection, the Museum of Modern Art, New York; gift of Frank Lloyd Wright.

Above left: Charles Rennie Mackintosh, one of the architect-furniture designers employing a Gothic simplicity in his work, used oak for this high-backed side chair of 1900. Collection, the Museum of Modern Art, New York; gift of the Glasgow School of Art.

Left: Naturalism produced new shaping in the Art Nouveau designs of Louis Majorelle and others. In this Majorelle card table the double legs, both curved from the rounded corners, and the pierced foliate design in the frieze show the sinuous charm of the period. *Lillian Nassau*

Above: Hector Guimard's African and olive ash desk, circa 1903, is an extraordinary play of curves both in the silhouette and in the base panels. Like a painter, Guimard applied a different abstract design on each differently scaled surface. Collection, the Museum of Modern Art, New York; gift of Mme. Hector Guimard.

Right: Walnut desk chair with leather seat by Hector Guimard, circa 1900, shows the same design as in the desk. Collection, the Museum of Modern Art, New York; gift of Mme. Hector Guimard.

chairs by Majorelle that were recently sold at Parke-Bernet have their roots in the Régence. The tie that binds the newer style with the old is the modeling of the subtly curved table legs and the flat carving on the chair and table frames.

Most of the Art Nouveau furniture auctioned here in recent seasons has been the work of Louis Majorelle and Emil Gallé. The dining table and chairs referred to above were by Majorelle. The table went for $400 and the twelve chairs for $1,400.

Another Majorelle design—an extraordinary sideboard with an arched superstructure shading open shelves and a base with open shelves and closed cupboards behind doors inlaid with flowering plant motifs—brought $1,150. Other designs in the same sale were a mahogany bookcase ($475), a walnut, stained glass and wrought iron armoire ($1,000), and a nest of inlaid mahogany tables at $225.

Early in 1969 Emil Gallé's work was auctioned, bringing equally low prices for the style that has caught the imagination of some of the more sophisticated collectors. Four tables were sold, all of which were embellished with inlays of naturalistic motifs. One with cherries and blossoms inset in the tabletop was $175. Lilacs and leaves covered the top of another, which was $185. A landscape appeared on the third, which sold for $175. Daffodils and a butterfly were worked into the decorative top of the fourth and most expensive—$325. Three of the four were signed, which makes the moderate prices even more unusual.

Since Art Nouveau furniture is a newcomer to the auction scene, these prices cannot be taken as a full indication of what one may pay in the future at public sale or in shops today. Specialists in the field believe that for signed or fine examples the prices will be more like those sold recently in a New York store: $475 for a plant stand and $575 for a chair.

part II

AMERICA

chapter 7

THE COLONIAL PERIOD
Puritan Era through Chippendale

~§ The Puritan period in the colonies, as far as furniture design and construction were concerned, is heavily overshadowed by the Jacobean and late Renaissance designs that existed at the same and earlier times in England and on the Continent.

The era is most often dated from 1650 to 1690 and is characterized by massive, primitive furniture forms. Chests that could be loaded onto wagons as families penetrated deeper and deeper into the wilderness that was America, are the most important furniture forms of this early period. Once the chest was settled inside the frame houses that were built by joiners and local carpenters or by the head of the household, it could serve as a storage piece, a seat or a tabletop. Its uses were, by necessity, varied in these sparsely furnished homes.

The chairs that appeared were equally formidable. The most frequently

A cradle believed to have rocked Peregrine White to sleep on the *Mayflower* is, surprisingly, fashioned of woven wicker. *Pilgrim Society, Plymouth, Mass. (The Dicksons photo)*

found design was the wainscot chair—a heavy, high-backed chair with boxy silhouette. These scaled-down thrones were reserved for the head of the household, and not all homes had them. Tables were of the trestle type, practical because they could be taken apart and loaded on a wagon as the settler moved on, or dismantled between meals to clear the center of the room where the family ate, slept, relaxed, and on rare occasions, entertained visitors.

The Great Migration, bringing sixty thousand Englishmen from villages that were rustic and still medieval in appearance and living style, to America in a single decade between 1630 and 1640, enriched the colonies with craftsmen of all skills. But the skills practiced in the English countryside were hardly so sophisticated as those known in London or in Paris in the same period. This partially accounts, of course, for the continuation in New England, New York and Jamestown of styles long since banished from the courts of aristocrats abroad.

Another reason for the lag in changing styles was the nostalgia early settlers shared for the lands they had left behind. In spite of the fact that these were people who had fled persecution in Europe, they longed for the amenities they had left behind. This yearning was echoed in the houses and furniture they built, and the tools and utensils they fashioned here.

Of course the rough-hewn, heavy furnishings of the Jacobean and late Renaissance styles were also better suited to demands made on artisans and to the harsh living conditions on this side of the Atlantic. What carpenters and carvers there were in the colonies, were busy turning their hands to shipbuilding, home construction and a variety of common tasks, leaving them little time for refining their skills to the same degree that cabinetmakers were doing in the capitals of Europe.

To further understand the furniture of this early time, one must examine the house where it was used. There were no grand castles or mansions in the colonies until the eighteenth century, when affluence spread and it became permissible, in fact desirable, for a man to show his wealth in the size and fineness of the house he built and the furnishings he used within its walls.

The earliest permanent houses were almost mirror images of Elizabethan dwellings. Heavy timbers, joined by mortise and tenon, served as the frame surrounding a massive fireplace. Casement windows filled with diamond-shaped, irregular glass panes or oiled paper, warded off the elements but did little to admit light.

Most homes had one large room downstairs where the cooking was done and the basic living and some sleeping accommodations were provided for. Upstairs were the sleeping quarters in most middle-class homes. In the winter the family gathered together in the main room, a miniature replica of the great halls of medieval castles, to warm themselves by the hearth. Upstairs chambers were used in the warmer months for other than sleeping needs. Visitors to a home often took tea in these upstairs quarters and, as noted in at least one diary of the period, even marriage ceremonies were performed there.

The early cupboards, made in the simple stile and rail construction of the day, are extremely difficult to find outside of museums and historic houses today. The few hundred that were made and did survive have long since gone back into the "public" domain. If such a storage piece is found, it would cost four to five figures today.

The smallest and most commonly found early chests are the Bible boxes. These portable boxes with lift-up lids or slant fronts were used to store the Bible, or when open, for reading or writing. The Bible box is America's earliest desk, and by the mid seventeenth century, there were complaints among the righteous that merchants were spending more time at it working on their ledgers than reading their Bibles.

One interesting feature of the Bible box is the owner's initials that usually were carved in the façade below the lock or around the keyhole. Other carving on the front panel was like that appearing on larger chests—tulips and other flowers, foliage and lunettes. These New England pieces were made mostly of oak and had pine tops, and originally they were painted. Vestiges of color remain on some pieces. Bible boxes can still be found on occasion for from $200 to $600.

The small chests of the period included the lift-up lid type used to store clothes, linens, books and other household possessions. One of the simplest is called the Ipswich chest, a style common in Europe in the Gothic period and in England throughout the Tudor and Jacobean eras. The pine-lidded oak chest is of stile and rail construction, and stands on short rectangular legs that are the terminations of the corner stiles. Front panels have flat carving, generally in floral or leaf motifs. Thomas Dennis of Ipswich, Massachusetts, made the style famous among his contemporaries and it is thought that it was copied in the New England area. Very few chests of this kind—or for that matter of the Hadley, sunflower, paneled or Guilford type—survive from the period. If found today, all would bring five figures if fine, four figures if of modest quality.

The Hadley chest, almost as rare as the Ipswich, was made in Hadley, Massachusetts, and is a variation in the form, having two drawers at the base, each extending between the stiles. They were used as hope chests are today. Most were finished to affect the look of ebony, with finishes devised with either stains or paint.

The Connecticut sunflower chest takes its name from the carvings of sunflowers, or occasionally asters, decorating the façade. Some chests also have bosses applied to the end panels and stiles decorated with strapwork or jewelwork, as the applied ornamentation was called. Like the Hadley chest, this one was usually, but not always, made with drawers below the chest space.

In addition to small chests, those colonial interpretations of the coffers of the Middle Ages, the average middle-class home was furnished with at least one large storage piece—a court or press cupboard. Both are forms from earlier times. The court cupboard is a tall, top-heavy Jacobean design with a cupboard on top and open space with one or two shelves below. The press cupboard is the design with cupboards and drawers built to the floor and supported on bun feet.

Trestle tables were the most common form of dining furniture in the seventeenth century. The one-board, plank top of up to twelve feet in length was set on a base of three T-shaped trestles that had beveled or chamfered edges. These were joined by a brace or stretcher that was slipped into the openings toward the base of each trestle. As pointed out above, these tables were extremely practical. When not in use between meals, the tops were removed, the bases dismantled, and the parts were stored to clear the floor for other uses in the main room of the house.

Early tables of this kind are practically impossible to find and command prices in four, possibly five figures. But as is discussed in the chapter on American country furniture, other similar sawbuck tables were made in rural areas up to and into the nineteenth century that might serve the same purpose in today's home.

In homes where space permitted and the living style demanded it, another smaller table with a drawer was found in this early period. Sometimes called the five-stretcher Cromwellian table, this rare design on turned legs was a New England specialty fashioned in the favorite local woods—maple or walnut, often with pine tops. The design is very like those made in previous decades in England and on the Continent, and if found would cost from $600 to $1,800 today.

The wainscot or solid-back chairs of the Puritan era bear an unmistakable resemblance to the English and continental designs of the sixteenth and seventeenth centuries. The New England wainscot chairs that have survived, particularly the elaborately carved designs by Thomas Dennis, the Ipswich joiner, were done in white oak, had flat top rails and were sometimes surmounted by carved crests and finials on the top rail and stiles.

One chair made between 1660 and 1700 by this master carver has carved scrolls framing the stiles, showing a softening of the severe, thronelike medieval silhouette. The entire back has the typical flat carving of grotesques, the carved figures of the Gothic era. Most of the early designs have squared legs, but some, like the elaborately carved Dennis wainscot chair, have lathe-turned legs. Arms end in scolls and are supported by the top of squared or baluster-turned front legs. Seats are flat and unpadded, although loose cushions were often used on them. Upholstery did not appear in the colonies until the end of the seventeenth century.

The seating accommodations in colonial homes were extremely modest and few in number. There was one chair for the master, but often others sat on chests, benches or the floor. However, some homes had Carver or Brewster chairs, named for early Massachusetts leaders because they owned the types named for them. The difference between the two is in the spindle arrangement in the chair back. The Brewster chair had a double row of spindles; the Carver had a single row. Both are discussed further, along with the Puritan three-legged chair, in the chapter on country furniture.

WILLIAM AND MARY

The William and Mary period in America, lasting from 1690 to 1720, released a new decorative force into cabinetmaking. The era might be said to have introduced the leggy look to furniture. It gave us the tall chest of drawers, later called the highboy, as well as its half-size cousin, the lowboy. It introduced wing chairs, daybeds, slant-top desks, gateleg, butterfly and tavern tables. It raised up the new, high-back chairs and the tables, chests, desks and cabinets on trumpet legs and ball, bun or turnip feet.

Leather and cane became major new chair coverings so much so that the financially-depressed textile makers requested Parliament to intercede in 1690 by legislating against caners to force them out of business. Japanning was the most visible evidence of the Oriental influences that were affecting furniture in England and on the continent. With the fashion for refinement came the

Above left: Carver chairs, like this New England example, had a single row of spindles across the back. Legs were joined by simply turned round rung stretchers. *Pilgrim Society, Plymouth, Mass.*

Above right: Brewster chairs had a double row of vertical spindles in the back (to contrast with the Carver chair, which had a single row of spindles). Although extremely simple in design, the chair is highly decorative in the turned spindles under the arms and seat. This Elder William Brewster chair shows that originally such designs also had spindles joining the stretchers at the base and middle of the legs. *Pilgrim Society, Plymouth, Mass.*

Right: Canework flourished in the colonies as it did in England in the late seventeenth, early eighteenth centuries. This William and Mary chair with cane seat and back panel and worn Spanish feet has a canted back with the crest rail centered with carved floral and shell motifs. It is from Rhode Island or Connecticut. *Thomas W. Carson, Salem, Mass.*

138

use of walnut, replacing oak, and of veneers. All contributed a new lightness to the look of furniture. Burl walnut was most frequently employed for veneers, as borders, and in some cases for such larger surfaces as drawer fronts.

This is the first baroque period in the New World. In the workshops where cabinetmakers still also functioned as carpenters and joiners, new opportunities offered artisans the chance to exercise skills unknown until then. Carving lost its primitive character, for it required far greater discipline than before to fashion the new shapely finials that sprouted on chair backs, table frames, highboys and tall-case clocks. The same increased skill was necessary to carve the pierced crests on the backs and on the front stretchers of chairs, the curved profile of the aprons on dressing tables, the X-shaped stretchers under tables and the arched moldings trimming drawer fronts.

The colonists were getting their first taste of affluence. The few well-to-do merchants and landowners wanted to have as much, or almost as much, ease and luxury as their kinsmen abroad. Many traveled, or at least heard from abroad of the latest fashions in clothing and furnishings, and were sophisticated enough to know how to have these designs translated into furnishings suited to the hardier climate and living habits of America.

The wing chair is possibly the single most important development in furniture of the William and Mary period. Called the easy chair when first introduced, this upholstered chair, padded through the seat and back, and provided with wings to ward off drafts, is a form still made today. With few exceptions, the wing chair remains one of the most comfortable forms of seating ever devised.

By the late seventeenth century, upholstering had become an established business in the colonies. Four upholstery shops existed in Boston by 1688 and probably an equally impressive number were making wing and other padded chairs in New York and Philadelphia in the same period..

Furniture, in spite of its move toward decoration, remained essentially as vertical in silhouette as in the previous Puritan period. Chairs and chests were tall with straight sides. Curves appeared in the carved crests on top rails or the turnings of legs, the flaring arms and the feet.

There was still a rigidity in furniture design, which is understandable. This is the period of the great moralist preachers like Cotton Mather. Where there is a stiffness in manners and morals, furniture will surely reflect it. What flights there were of decorative fancy in this period, were restricted to the marquetry on flat surfaces of chests, the play of fine woods—of burl walnut and other veneers on slant-front desks—and in the new japanner's craft.

Japanning is the substitute for lacquer developed on the Continent and in England when lacquered products from the Far East were all the rage in Europe. The practice came about as the demand for lacquered products from the East kept increasing and the English East India Company was not able to fill the orders. And in spite of the demand, prices remained excessively high for these goods.

High-backed, leather-covered maple armchair of the William and Mary period was made in New York, possibly for Peter Schuyler, in the beginning of the era of upholstery. The pierced crest surmounting the chair back, and the carved front stretcher are of foliate and scroll designs. The arms flare outward, ending in scrolls. *Courtesy of The Henry Ford Museum, Dearborn, Mich.*

Boston chairs, like this New England version made around 1700, were a flourishing business in the colonies. The maple example covered in leather stands on button feet. *Courtesy of The Henry Ford Museum, Dearborn, Mich.*

The publication in England of *A Treatise of Japanning and Varnishing* by John Stalker and George Parker was the seventeenth century's do-it-yourself manual for cabinetmakers. The substitute for the lacquered products gave us figurative decoration of low relief, formed with gesso and finished with metal leaf on black and red painted ground. The japanned work produced here from the beginning of the eighteenth century, like that produced abroad, was profusely embellished with chinoiserie decoration. Camels and other real or imaginary animals and birds, as well as Oriental flower arrangements, people and houses figured in the fantastic designs.

It was in this period that rural craftsmen were developing other important traditional furniture forms and decorative treatments that affected decoration on furniture. The banister-back chair is a case in point. It had Spanish feet, curled arm ends, carved and pierced crests on top rails. Instead of the costly caned back and seat, there were flat wood spindles forming the banister back and a rush seat. As a substitute for marquetry, veneers and japanning, rural artisans painted the façades of furniture with stylized fruit and flowers that are anything but Oriental.

Walnut was the favorite wood throughout the William and Mary and Queen Anne periods. But maple was also very important and was used frequently for the japanned pieces made here.

Most of the furniture of the William and Mary period is not only difficult to find but is costly. The so-called Restoration or caned chairs of this period successfully eclipsed the popularity of the wainscot, Carver and Brewster chairs and relegated the slat-back chair to rural areas. The cane chair had its back panel set in a scroll-carved wood frame that was fixed between turned stiles and under a carved or pierced crest. The seat is rectangular. Legs are turned in ring-and-knob patterns and on finer designs, in trumpet-and-ball shapes. The side and back stretchers are turned and the front stretcher is a carved or pierced crested panel.

The Boston chair produced in the William and Mary style from the early eighteenth century up until the Revolution was a special type of spoon-back or contour-backed chair with leather-covered backs and seats. The backs are far simpler than the fine William and Mary chairs, but the vertical form remains. The frame is uncarved, save for the front legs which are lathe-turned and have Spanish or button feet. Back legs are canted and the stretchers are plain, save for the front one which has ball turnings. Made in maple and painted red or black, these chairs were popular throughout the colonies and were even exported abroad.

In the Queen Anne period, these designs began to be copied in other cities, particularly Philadelphia. And with the advent of the cabriole leg, a cross-breeding, common in transitional styles, occurred. The basic Boston chair frame continued, but the seat and back were often caned, the front legs were curved, and the seat apron was carved. The front stretcher disappeared and was replaced by a turned stretcher between the two side stretchers.

The banister-back chair was another durable seating design that persisted until the Revolution, and was revived again in the twentieth century. The backs were made of from three to six half spindles, flat on the front and rounded on the back. The name refers to the resemblance of the chair back to a banister rail, a corruption of the word balusters, which mean the spindles supporting the handrail of a staircase.

The half spindles of the banister-back chair were made by taking two pieces of wood, gluing them together and then turning them on a lathe to get vase or ring-and-ball turnings. The pieces were then separated and the half spindles fitted to the chair back.

Banister-back chairs were made with Spanish or button feet terminations on turned legs. Arm versions have the typical scroll ends of the period and back frames are also sometimes lathe-turned in ring-and-ball, vase-and-ring, bobbin or plain vase patterns. Seats are rush or splint. Surviving examples of early versions bring $400 to $2,000 today. But the later, country versions cost far less —from $75 to $300.

The daybed is a new furniture form in this period and derives its shape from the chairs of the era. Many were made with cane seat and back panels, some had adjustable panels that dropped back on chains. This is one of the many indications in furniture design in the early eighteenth century of the increasing desire for ease and comfort. The Restoration daybed is associated with the cane-paneled designs and the William and Mary with the vase splat versions.

Left: Banister-backed chairs were extremely popular in the colonial period. This painted example from 1690–1720 was fashioned of pine, maple and oak in Rhode Island. The Spanish feet, turned legs and stretchers, arms ending in scrolls and carved back crest rail frame the rush seat. *Courtesy of The Henry Ford Museum, Dearborn, Mich.*

Below: William and Mary daybed, a new furniture form in this period, is a painted blue walnut design with woven seat and an adjustable back. The Pennsylvania design, circa 1700, stands on turned legs joined by turned stretchers. *Courtesy of The Henry Ford Museum, Dearborn, Mich.*

William and Mary daybeds were made with eight turned legs supporting the extended seat, the back two of which are continuations of the chair back. On Restoration daybeds this feature does not exist.

Tables also show a decided emphasis on refinement, and the variety of types made testifies to the change of living habits in the colonial home. No longer is it necessary to make do, to have trestle tables that can be taken apart and put away when not in use. The forests have been cleared, and the settler is now a property owner who intends to remain and cultivate a life sweetened with material comforts.

The gateleg table is a drop-leaf design that was introduced in the late seventeenth century. From the start the swing-out base had oval or oblong tops. The gateleg derives its name from the gatelike swing to the two legs that serve as supports for the drop leaves when the table is opened. Walnut was the wood most used, but many were also of maple or cherry. Modest examples can probably be found for $500, but fine ones command $3,000 today.

Butterfly tables were also new in the period. Their similarity to the joined stool leads one to believe that they evolved from the use of the joined stool as an occasional table. In the William and Mary period these tables had wing supports for leaves. Baluster-shaped legs are splayed and joined by squared stretchers. The table was made mostly in New England until 1730 and brings $500 to $2,000 today at auction or in shops.

One must be wary of copies of these tables, made in the 1920's. Forty years of use can give wood the worn look and something of the patina of older pieces. But an examination of the construction will settle the matter, for the twentieth-century copies were made by machine. Another telltale sign of older tables is the worn condition of the feet. Early ones are also quite likely to have vestiges of red filler, a popular finish on the maple, cherry and walnut woods employed.

Slant-front desks, both on frames and on chests, were also new to furniture in this period. The desk-on-frame looks very much like the earlier Bible boxes set on tables and no doubt developed from the increased use of this design in that manner. The emphasis on desks at the end of the seventeenth century also shows the change from physical to more mental pursuits among the colonists.

American men of letters would soon begin to rival those in England and on the Continent. The intellectual emphasis is probably even more apparent with the introduction of the bureau desk. A sense of permanence is suggested by the solidity of the design—a desk set on top of a chest of drawers that was used to store papers. The bureau—a term that came to mean a chest of drawers in nineteenth-century America—as stated earlier, evolved from the Louis XIII period when tables covered with *bure,* a kind of fabric, were used to write on.

The interior of the desk is fitted neatly with dividers and drawers. Refinements, like the occasional arched tops over the pigeonholes, also appear. Most of these early New England walnut and maple desks stand on ball feet. Today

The Dutch influence persisted in New York furniture, as can be seen in the heavy proportions and ball feet on this New York secretary with a fall-front writing surface made in the late seventeenth or early eighteenth century. The William and Mary design is inlaid with marquetry in a charmingly wrought floral design. *Museum of the City of New York*

they are not common, but are, for their age, relatively inexpensive, ranging from $600 to $2,000.

The high chest of drawers on legs that came to be known in the nineteenth century as a highboy, was immediately popular in the colonies following its appearance here in the late seventeenth century. The convenience of not having

William and Mary dressing table standing on trumpet legs ending in shapely bun feet is a New England design in walnut and walnut veneer made between 1700 and 1720. The lowboy has the typical drops flanking the kneehole and an X-shaped curved stretcher. *Courtesy of The Henry Ford Museum, Dearborn, Mich.*

to stoop to open a drawer made this a most desirable furnishing among the convenience-conscious colonists. The elegant appearance of this leggy design (five or six legs were used) added to its strong attraction. These flat-topped tall chests were made with four tiers of five drawers in the top section, and either one large or three smaller drawers in the base part. Carved aprons can be seen on finer versions and, on occasion, conceits appear, such as a hidden drawer in the molding below the overhanging top edge.

Highboys were made with Flemish scroll legs on bun feet or trumpet legs on ball or bun feet. Walnut was most favored, but some were made in maple. Veneers decorated fine versions and less sophisticated designs often were executed in pine, basswood or tulipwood and painted to simulate walnut. Period highboys generally run high, from $800 to $3,000 or more.

The lowboy, also new in the seventeenth century, looks like the lower segment of the highboy. But in the William and Mary period, the pieces were not necessarily made to match each other as they were later in the eighteenth century. The lowboy functioned most often as a dressing table. It bore trumpet-

The William and Mary high chest of drawers, like this New England maple and walnut veneer design made between 1700 and 1720, stood on trumpet and cup legs joined by curved stretchers. This example belonged to George Washington's mother, Mary Ball Washington. *Courtesy of The Henry Ford Museum, Dearborn, Mich.*

146

and-vase or trumpet-and-cup legs ending in ball or bun feet. Legs were joined by a carved, X-shaped or cross stretcher.

The skirt of the lowboy, like that of the high chest, was carved in arches or scalloped. It was also often embellished with carved drops flanking the kneehole in the place of the legs used in that position on the highboy. Generally the piece has three drawers placed side by side, with the shallowest drawer in the center. Lowboys range from about $700 to $2,000 today. More moderate-priced designs should be carefully checked for construction details because the lowboy, revived forty years ago, will in some cases have acquired an aged appearance that could be misread as 1720, not 1920.

WINDSOR

The Windsor chair, which probably dates from the late seventeenth century, is an anachronism in the history of furniture design. This assemblage of a wood plank and sticks, reverses the pattern of design development. Almost without exception, great and enduring furniture designs were, in ages past, created for the nobility, and more recently for art patrons furnishing important houses or large corporations building new offices. They were and are expensive and finely made of choice materials. When copied, their forms and the materials used in them were of lesser interest and quality. These copies almost invariably are less costly than the originals.

In the case of the Windsor, the whole pattern of its evolution is quite the opposite. Its form appears to be unknown before the late seventeenth century when the itinerant English furniture makers fashioned spindles, legs, bows, stretchers and seats in their movable workshops, traveling from one place to another as the marketing demands changed. One story of its rise from obscurity to widespread popularity credits George II with admiring one he saw in a country cottage near Windsor Castle. In all histories of furniture, it is emphasized that this "stick furniture"—sticks for the back, sticks for the legs and stretchers and a plank seat—has no precedent on the Continent. If the name does not derive from the George II story, it probably comes from the marketing town of Windsor in Buckinghamshire near High Wycombe where the chair has been made for two hundred years.

The Windsor was, at first, a humble chair made probably of beech and pine in the early years of the eighteenth century. It was for use by the middle classes in their cottages and farmhouses as well as for aristocrats to be enjoyed in their gardens. They were painted green, red or yellow, both as a protection against the rain and to conceal the undistinguished wood. Josiah Wedgwood owned Windsors for which he is said to have paid 5 or 6 shillings apiece. Because they are moderate in price and durable, they became then, and remain today, a popular form of seating for public eating places.

By the second quarter of the eighteenth century, London cabinetmakers were producing finer mahogany versions for drawing rooms, dressing up the

Hoop-back Windsor chair with pierced cresting, baluster supports under the arms and canted legs is an ash and elm English design made about 1820. *Corner Shop, Macy's, New York*

Ash and elm comb-back Windsor, made in England about 1780, is a relatively simple country version, commonly found in shops in America and in England. *Corner Shop, Macy's, New York*

rustic design with a pierced splat in the back, often topped by a wheellike medallion, and supported on cabriole legs. Even St. James's Palace was furnished with Windsor chairs.

By 1725 the Windsor had arrived in America, and from that date through the nineteenth century, a seemingly unending parade of variations was created that are judged far more imaginative and decorative than their English forebears.

American cabinetmakers seem to have understood the Windsor form better than English artisans. Although the chair was to enjoy popularity inside and outside the home, it never lost its basic simplicity, as it did in the land of its birth.

Windsors derive their strength and durability from the rustic way they are made. Splayed legs of such easy-to-turn woods as close-grained maple, birch, ash or chestnut were set into plank seats made from unseasoned lumber. This "green" wood seat, generally of pine or whitewood, was soft enough to carve in contour or even saddle shapes.

No screws or nails were used in well-made Windsors. The legs and back spindles were set into the seat from below and above, and when the wood seat shrank, it gripped the component parts, creating one of the sturdiest forms of furniture construction ever devised.

The first American Windsors were the low-backs. These, as their name suggests, have short rods, supporting a rounded continuous bow that formed the arms and top rail. In the early nineteenth century these chairs came to be known as firehouse chairs but today they are most often called captain's chairs. They, like the comb-backs that followed, were first made in Philadelphia. The comb-backs were similar to the low-back, but had an upper layer of spindles at the back, topped by a thin, bow-shaped rail that did not connect with the arm rail. Bow-backs and hoop-backs, like the comb-backs, have an upper layer of spindles at the back, with the top rail curved downward on the sides and joined with the armrests.

Fanback Windsors have doubly long back spindles going from the seat to the top rail which, as on comb-backs, ends in a Cupid's bow rail. A modest New England fanback side chair sold recently for $200. The hoop-back is an armless design that has long back spindles. The back is topped by a loop-shaped rail bent on the sides to end in the seat.

The variety of combinations of these basic types include the New England writing-arm Windsors with bow-, comb- or brace-backs, and triple backs, chairs that look like combination comb- and bow-backs.

By 1750 the fabrication of Windsor chairs began to spread to every city on the Eastern coast and soon became one of the most popular furnishings in the colonies. It was a chair admired by the high- and lowborn. Thomas Jefferson is believed to have sat in a Windsor when drafting the Declaration of Independence. An engraving by Edward Savage exists showing the Second Continental Congress at work in hoop-backs. George Washington paid $1.78 each in 1796 for the twenty-seven he bought to furnish the portico at Mt. Vernon.

Becoming an expert on Windsors requires a knowledge of where each type is from, told by the shaping of the legs or the special curve of the arms. The Philadelphians liked boldly turned legs and ball feet. Bamboo turnings appear on New England chairs. Others were shaped like tenpins. The writing-arm Windsors—with drawers placed under the writing shelf and sometimes under the seat too, were abundant in New England. Ward Beecher, the father of Harriet Beecher Stowe, owned a very distinctive writing-arm Windsor, with an unusually wide writing tablet, a drawer beneath and a very high back. Because of its distinction of form and the known provenance of the chair, it was offered recently at an unusually high price for a Windsor—$3,200.

A mark of quality to watch for in selecting Windsors is the number of spindles. Nine is excellent, and eleven is rare and exceptional. The shaping of the seat, the degree of boldness in the leg turnings and the angling of the legs (the greater the splay, the better) are other equally important characteristics.

This New Jersey stick Windsor, made about 1800, has bamboo-turned back spindles and is covered with sponge decoration in red, black and yellow. *Elizabeth Stokes, Weare, N.H.*

The Windsor form has always been used for children's furniture. This nineteenth-century child's high chair is an excellent hand-crafted example. *The Place on Second Avenue, New York*

The American Windsors, like their English cousins, were painted green for the most part. But red, black, yellow, rose, gray, brown, blue or white were also made and some were even patterned with flowers. Thomas Jefferson ordered four dozen in black and gold for Monticello, and Benjamin Franklin had two dozen painted white.

Because Windsors were produced for such a long period, they are available in relative abundance. But in many cases the common versions are difficult for amateurs to date. Prices will range from a few dollars for a captain's chair of the nineteenth century to well up in four figures for fine versions.

By the Victorian age there were spindle-backed dining-room Windsors, spindle-backed side chairs, splat-backed Windsors and writing armchairs (the captain's chair with a rounded arm for working).

A very few other types of furnishings were developed based on the Windsor chair. Settees with hoop backs or low backs, cradles and three-legged tables are among the Windsor-type furnishings. But these rare designs are almost impossible to find in shops and at auctions.

QUEEN ANNE

Graceful is the word most furniture historians use to describe the Queen Anne style, which appeared here first in 1710 and reigned supreme from 1720 to 1750. Indeed one is hard put to find a more apt description of the style that brought us chairs with the cabriole leg, the shell and acanthus carving on crested top rails, the vase-shaped splat, the horseshoe seat, and the serpentine seat fronts.

In England the period marked the beginning of the golden age of cabinet-work, a time when the surface ornament gave way to an emphasis on fine woods carved in low relief. Form dominates and the fantastic carving feats that had been seen in the William and Mary period disappear.

Furniture suddenly began to melt into curves, not fussy turns and twists as would happen later in the Chippendale rococo designs that followed, but strong, sweeping, undulating lines that showed a firm hand and bold imagination.

Queen Anne was the period when the chair began to conform to the body, became more comfortable and lent an element of ease rather than forbidding solidity to a room. The black walnut and maple woods employed are carved less for decorative effect than to show the beauty and finish of the wood itself.

Shells and sunrise or sunburst carvings, the latter two occasionally used together, dominate the carvings that appeared on crested chair rails, chest fronts and curved knees of cabriole legs. The cushioned, disklike Dutch pad or club foot was one of the many leg supports favored in the period. Others were the trifid foot, which had three toelike points, and the snake and the slipper foot, so-called because of their shapes.

Furniture visibly lightens in form and carving, bringing distant echoes of the fantastic shapes and embellishments favored in the Palladian villas of England and on the Continent in the same era. But the colonists were too sober to embrace the exaggerations of the style shown in the gilt and elaborately carved Queen Anne designs. It was the beginning of the era in which fortunes were made and great houses built. In the Chippendale period, affluence became more commonplace and the new "society" was far less timid about showing their wealth.

Certain antique and foreign elements figured in the shaping of the Queen Anne style. Oriental influences can be seen in the solid, contoured splat back, a feature of Ming chairs, and in the use of vaselike details, which many experts trace to Chinese vases. The ball-and-claw foot, which emerged late in the period, has its roots in the Oriental dragon holding a pearl, an ancient device. The acanthus leaf and the scallop shell spring from such earlier classic cultures as the Italian Renaissance, the Phoenician, the Greek and the Roman.

Philadelphia was the seat of the finest American cabinetwork in the colonies

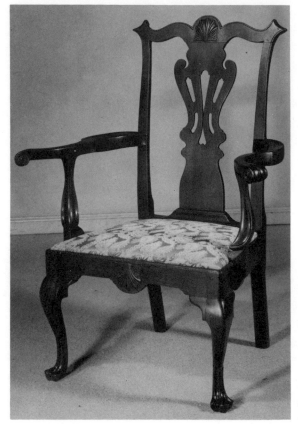

From its Cupid's bow crest rail to its trifid feet, this Philadelphia Queen Anne arm chair is the essence of grace. The pierced vasiform splat, the ogival arms and the shell-carved apron show the early eighteenth-century Pennsylvania craftsman's skills. *Parke-Bernet Galleries*

throughout the Queen Anne and Chippendale periods. It was there that the most exuberant forms of both styles were created. In most cases, the Philadelphia designs were closer to the European versions of the style than the variations made in other cities. Chairs had arms that snaked in double reverse curves from chair backs that were more precisely scrolled in fiddleback design than elsewhere. Animalistic cabriole legs were topped by finer leafy knees that ended in sock-covered feet. This detail was very much in the Irish taste.

As profuse in ornament as the Philadelphia designs were, so spare and meticulously executed were the Boston chairs, chests and tables. The ample interpretation of the style in New York might well be credited to the comfort-conscious Dutch. In both New York and Newport the use of the shell-on-crest for the embellishment of chairs was favored. But in New England a lighter hand was evident in the fashioning of serpentine stretchers. In Connecticut, turned stretchers joined the squat cabriole legs, backs were wider and more simply carved than in any other colonial workshops and curved seat skirts were favored.

The vase-splat chair is the most frequently seen seating design in the period from 1710 to 1725. It was copied over and over in country chairs into the

The wing chair, never so superb as in the Queen Anne period, exudes a sense of comfort and of grace. The canted back, out-scrolling arms and cabriole legs on pad feet joined by turned stretchers of this early eighteenth-century example show why. *Parke-Bernet Galleries*

nineteenth century and again by mass producers in Southern factories in the twentieth century.

In its simplest form, the vase-splat chair has a rush seat, turned legs in either vase-and-ring or ring-and-knob patterns ending in Spanish feet joined by a stretcher carved and turned in front in the ring-and-ball design. Arm versions of the style have flat, scrolled rests and handgrips. Maple was the wood most favored, but the chair was made in other hardwoods and sometimes was finished with red filler. In spite of its rusticity, this chair is not inexpensive, commanding $300 to $700 each. Examples made through the mid eighteenth century are more commonly found and cost from $100 to $300.

The better-known vase-splat chair, made through the peak years of the Queen Anne period, has a spooned back, so called because it matched the curve of the spine and stood on cabriole legs. The top rail is arched, the seat, shield-shaped. Walnut, maple and other woods were used for this design, which today carries price tags from $200 to $700.

Scrolled fiddleback chairs are considerably richer in detail, with curved back frames, cabriole legs with Dutch or trifid feet and shell, or leaf-carved knees. The colonists made this style extremely popular and in each region different characteristics appeared. Examples can be found in walnut or mahogany at from $2,000 down to $300.

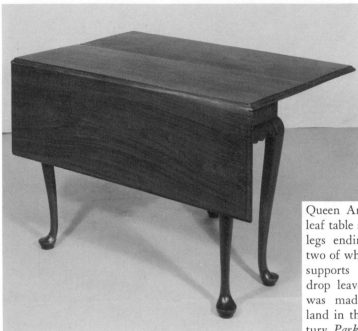

Queen Anne walnut drop-leaf table stands on cabriole legs ending in spade feet, two of which swing as gate supports when the two drop leaves are in use. It was made in New England in the eighteenth century. *Parke-Bernet Galleries*

Queen Anne wing chairs are considered by many to be the acme of the chair form. The free-flowing curve from the winged back into the arms ending in a scrolled armrest is a shaping that by mid-century was to be replaced by far less graceful forms. Upholstered wing chairs are not as easy to find as wood-framed seating, and cost from $500 to $4,000.

"Roundabout" is the term given the right-angled corner chair of this era. These low-backed chairs had two splats between three spindles joined by a crested top rail. They were embellished with modest to elaborate shell carvings on the knees and had Spanish scroll feet. Later claw-and-ball feet served as the supports. Both modest and extremely fine versions were made, designs that are available today from $200 to $500.

The daybed continued to be a design to be reckoned with in the Queen Anne period. Like the vase-splat chair, the daybed has cabriole legs, a squared and canted back frame. Eight legs joined by bobbin-turned stretchers were required as base supports. Woods favored were walnut and cherry, and in later years mahogany was sometimes used. This rare design carries commensurate price tags, from $800 to $5,000 or even more today.

Even rarer and more costly are the Queen Anne sofas that are fashioned like Queen Anne wing chairs—without the wings. In their place, however, are ear-like ends that flare out from the sofa back. Two cabriole legs serve as the front supports, and three squared and canted legs appear at the back.

Tables came into wider use in the Queen Anne period, and the cabinetmakers produced an abundance of variations to meet the popular taste. Drop-leaf tables with rectangular, oval or round tops stand on cabriole legs, two of which swing out to support the leaves when the table is extended. Today prices range from $400 to $5,000. Not long ago a drop-leaf dining table made in Massachusetts brought $3,000 at auction.

Other smaller tables—the tray tops, tea, sideboard and gaming tables, to mention a few—were made in most of the colonies in varying degrees of quality. In all types, there are differences in apron carvings, shapes of the tops and feet terminations. Tea tables are among the easiest to find, but their prices can rise to extraordinary heights, as was proven recently. A New England table was $2,500 and a Connecticut table was $7,750. Less costly finds can, of course, be made, at from about $500 up. And less-prized tables, like the porringer-top table that went for $850, might be sought by collectors with thinnish purses.

Chests were a major furnishing in colonial homes. Among the many types made were the chest-on-frame, the low chest, the highboy and the lowboy. The two-section, chest-on-frame had a flat top, but highboys came with flat or bonnet tops. The low chests are also the lowest in price (from $300 into four figures). The bonnet-topped highboys can run well up into four figures, and on occasion into five. A chest-on-frame recently sold for $1,500. In the same sale, a maple lowboy brought $575. But finer cherrywood lowboys have recently brought $9,500 and $5,500, the higher-priced one emanating from Philadelphia, and the one at lower cost, from New England.

Several types of desks were made in the Queen Anne period; none was new in design. The box-on-a-base was made in such variations as the slant-front desk on turned frame, the sloping-lid desk on turned frame, the countinghouse desk and the slant-front desk on cabriole leg frame. All were, or looked as if they were, made in two parts. With the exception of the countinghouse desk, which was made into the nineteenth century, Queen Anne desks flourished between 1720 and 1750. As with most examples of this period, prices cover a wide range. Lucky shoppers may find good desks for as low as $200 or $500, but most shops have higher price tags on writing desks—from $800 to $7,000, and more for fine-quality designs.

The bureaus and secretaries are even more expensive and harder to find in today's marketplace. Both types were made with cabriole legs or bracket feet, had internal fittings of pigeonholes, drawers, doored enclosures and, in the case of secretaries, were made with flat or bonnet tops.

Queen Anne beds, those tester-framed designs with cabriole or squared legs, are very rare indeed today, as they were in the period. Only the finest homes had such beds. Most were made by better cabinetmakers and even in poor condition would command $700 today, but top prices will more than likely be $5,000 and up.

Flat-topped Queen Anne high chest (highboy) fashioned in cherrywood in New England has a projecting molded cornice, a gracefully shaped apron centered by a carved fan, and stands on cabriole legs ending in claw-and-ball feet. *Parke-Bernet Galleries*

156

Although simpler than many Queen Anne lowboys, this cherrywood example made in Philadelphia in the early eighteenth century is superb. The shaped apron and the shell-carved cabriole legs ending in drake feet are uncommonly fine. *Parke-Bernet Galleries*

Queen Anne secretary made in Connecticut between 1730 and 1750 is a cherry design with stylized floral carving on the upper stiles, shell carving centering the apron at the base. *Courtesy of The Henry Ford Museum, Dearborn, Mich.*

CHIPPENDALE

The Chippendale period in America is a distinctive mixture of old and new, of imitative and individualistic details. The rococo style, borrowed from the English interpretations of the French styles, reigned here from 1750 until the eve of the American Revolution in 1775. It is well to remember that in England, in its day, the style we now call Chippendale was alternately described as Gothic, Chinese, modern, and in the French taste.

With Chippendale comes the beginning of the mahogany age, a wood that remained undisputed king until the Empire period nurtured a taste for the more exotic rosewood. During this period, such echoes of Queen Anne as the claw-and-ball foot, a late bloomer in America, continued to flourish. Actually Thomas Chippendale ignored the claw-and-ball foot in all editions of his *The Gentleman and Cabinet-Maker's Director,* published first in 1754 and revised and expanded in 1759 and 1762. Although not the first of such pattern books, it became the most important manual of furniture and decorations issued

The pierced splat and molded top rail, the heavy acanthus leaf-carved knees and claw-and-ball feet on this New York Chippendale side chair are typical of the style as seen about 1760 in the Dutch colony. Note the gadrooning detail on the apron. *Museum of the City of New York*

In Philadelphia the Chippendale chairs were fashioned most closely to the English designs of that day. This one with a flaring back and serpentine crest rail centered by a shell has a vasi-form splat and stands on shell-carved cabriole legs ending in claw-and-ball feet. *Parke-Bernet Galleries*

up to that date. It also marked the break with the architecture-oriented Queen Anne style. The drawings shown of furniture alone—that is, removed from rooms—are significant.

Expert cabinetmakers based in and around Philadelphia, Newport, New York and Boston clung to the heavy yet simple carved termination of the cabriole leg. They preferred the claw-and-ball to the more elaborate scroll foot that Thomas Chippendale had established as a mid eighteenth-century fashion in London.

The highboy is another example of the lingering influence of the Queen Anne style on American Chippendale furniture. This imposing furniture form had already been discarded as passé in England. Yet it continued to evolve and reached its pinnacle of development in the hooded or bonnet-topped versions made in the second half of the eighteenth century.

Nevertheless the *Director* and several other pattern books by English cabinetmakers served, by and large, as the bibles of the furniture craftsmen at work in the colonies in this period. From the pages of Chippendale's design book sprang the Pembroke tables—those drop-leaf space-savers that so enchanted late eighteenth- and early nineteenth-century Americans; and the Marlborough leg, that fluted, molded, fretted or plain and squared underpinning of the so-called Chinese Chippendale chairs and tables. The pierced splat-back chairs that were so popular in London were also highly successful here. The carved open work on these chair backs was only possible because of the native mahogany used, a fact that Philadelphia craftsmen understood better than most of their colonial colleagues.

Chippendale's influence added new designs to the parlors and bedrooms of American homes. Tilt-top, tray-top and tripod-based tea tables, kneehole writing desks, and linen presses answered the demands for new conveniences and facilities in the home.

The colonial craftsman, always an artisan with an individualistic bent, began in the second half of the eighteenth century to cut the cords that bound him to England. No group showed more originality in this movement than Newport's three generations of Townsends and Goddards, those highly esteemed cabinet-makers who were closely related by intermarriage.

In their hands, the block-front chest with its shell carving and the kneehole desk reached a degree of vigor and artistry unmatched on these designs anywhere else in the world. The nineteen members of this seaport dynasty who contributed to this evolution also fashioned claw-and-ball feet with a distinctive difference from those of their American colleagues. Newport, it must be remembered, was a cultivated, progressive harbor in that day, a center of foreign trade that surpassed New York in volume. In the designs by the Townsends and Goddards, the claw is raised above the ball and joined to it at the nails, a conceit permitting light to pass through the foot and showing what superb craftsmen these men were.

If Newport had its block-front and special claw-and-ball foot, Massachusetts also had its special furniture design attributes. The slender cabriole legs with pointed knees and claws on the feet turned back as if tenaciously gripping the ball are two. Another characteristic of Massachusetts furniture is the shaped, decorative façades of chests. Two cabinetmakers known for their craftsmanship in this period are John Cogswell and Benjamin Frothingham. Their kettle-based or bombé façades, japanned surfaces, chinoiserie motifs, French scroll and hairy paw feet were typical local devices.

In New York the accent in cabinetry was on choice, if heavy, carving, sturdiness, comfort and generous proportions. An echo of the Dutch heritage appeared in the gadrooning on chair skirts. The distinctive, boxlike claw-and-ball, the variety of straight or curved chest fronts, the early appearance of squared, straight legs are other characteristics. The chest-on-chest, rather than the highboy, was a regional favorite. Spider-leg tables, like the English modifications of gateleg tables, were also common to the area.

Of all the centers of cabinetmaking, Philadelphia produced the most exuberant carving. In this government and mercantile center, the taste for richness of detail was closer to London than anywhere else in the colonies. As the largest city (its population tripled between 1750 and 1775), it had some of the most sophisticated cabinetmakers who frowned openly on any of the local citizenry who chose to import English goods. Jonathan Gostelowe, Thomas Affleck, Benjamin Randolph (who worked for Thomas Jefferson), William Savery, James Gillingham and Thomas Tufft were among the best of the local artisans. They, and others, consciously emphasized their carving skills by toning down the proportions of the designs they executed and allowing the surface carving greater importance.

Chests were shorter, legs were sometimes almost squat. Yet, in spite of the extravagant detailing, the silhouettes of the pieces always dominated as they did on all fine American cabinetry produced in this period.

American Chippendale at its finest could hardly be called provincial. There were, of course, country interpretations of the style, further simplified with crude carving. But these, and the finer designs made for city and country mansions, which sometimes rivaled the elegant way of life on English country estates, are not easily found in antiques shops and at auctions.

A New England slant-front desk of the Chippendale period frequently was fitted within with arcaded pigeonholes and fan-carved, block-front drawers. This example even has a secret drawer. At the base is a scroll-carved pendant centering a molded apron standing on claw-and-ball feet. *Parke-Bernet Galleries*

Today fine American Chippendale commands prices far beyond English designs and far beyond what the average collector can pay for the style. Country versions of the style, although often made after the period, are where the collector will find well-priced purchases. Chairs of even modest quality from the period cost $150 up into four figures. This includes pierced splat-back, ladder-back and wing chairs and armchairs. A Philadelphia shell-carved design recently sold for the not very surprising sum of $1,600. Sets of dining chairs have been priced at from $2,000 to $7,000 over the first several months of 1969. A wing chair brought $1,200 and a Philadelphia sofa, $2,400.

Pembroke tables, those narrow, drop-leaf tables with squared legs, rectangular tops, and X-shaped stretcher bases stem from what we now call the Chinese Chippendale period and were made from 1750 to 1790. They were a specialty in this country and were fashioned in mahogany, cherry or maple. Today such tables made in the era are from $400 to $3,000 in shops, with extremely fine examples commanding more and lesser examples even lower prices. Two Pembrokes were recently sold for the top price and one for $350 at Parke-Bernet sales.

The variety of small tilt-top, tray-top, dish-top, and piecrust tables on cabriole-legged, pedestal bases is astounding in this era. There seems to be a table for every possible need executed in several tasteful variations. All this abundance testifies to the increasing affluence and refinement of living habits, as well as to the skills of craftsmen in furniture workshops of the period. Although most of the forms are not original with Chippendale, it was in this period that such tables came into popular use.

One of the most common and least expensive tables found today is the tilt-top candlestand, a small circular-topped table, which generally brings $200 and more. Auctions, surprisingly, are not the best place to shop for these tables, judging by recent sales where few were included and the prices ran as high as $575 for those offered.

The larger, plain and circular-topped tables cost from $300 up. Piecrust tables with fluted edges are very rare and may well command from $2,000 to $10,000. But plain piecrust designs can be found for $500 and up. Tilt-tops in other shapes are available from $400.

Drop-leaf dining tables, another form that had wide acceptance in the epoch, cost $500 to $2,000 today. The rectangular tables used as sideboards in dining rooms are from $200 for country versions to $15,000 for the finer products of known makers' shops. Gaming tables in tilt-top, pedestal-based form can be found for from $300 to five figures. A Philadelphia card table commanded $3,000 at a recent auction in New York.

Chests of drawers took on strong regional characteristics during the Chippendale period. Although the chests often had serpentine or oxbow curved fronts, the New York penchant for the straight front did not waver. Examples

Chippendale linen press by Matthew Egerton, New Brunswick, N.J., was made in two parts. The upper cupboard is flanked by fluted and canted stiles; the lower is fitted with molded drawers and stands on bracket feet. *Parke-Bernet Galleries*

may be found today for from $450 to four figures. One fine Philadelphia version was sold for $2,500 recently, and another went for $4,000.

It was this interest in the chest that probably paved the way for the Chippendale bureau desk, which also had regional characteristics. There were the straight or serpentine fronts standing on bracket or claw-and-ball foot bases. The designs with slant-front writing surfaces had graduated drawers. Those with bracket feet cost today from $600 well up into four figures, whereas the cabriole-legged, claw-and-ball foot versions command $1,500 to $5,000 or more.

The square-legged, slant-front desk, very like the schoolmaster's or bookkeeper's desk that would continue to be made into the nineteenth century, generally has one drawer and a carved apron below it. Although not many were made, this desk is a far more modest Chippendale design than most, costing from $200 to $1,500. A cherry-wood slant-front was tagged at $600 not long ago, an average price one might expect to pay for this design at auction or in better shops.

Highboys, known as high chests in the eighteenth century, may have lost popularity in England, but in America they were greatly admired. This esteem resulted in some of the finest carving. The stunning Philadelphia highboys have their tops whipped smartly into bonnet shapes, their bases handsomely fashioned into cabriole legs with shell-carved knees and claw-and-ball feet. Façades were embellished with carved foliage, shells and even scenes from Aesop's fables, an idea from Chippendale's *Director*. Even lesser examples of this furniture form command $700 and fine ones rise high in five figures. At a sale early in 1969 a Philadelphia highboy brought a record price of $60,000. Earlier, a Pennsylvania one commanded $11,000. But a walnut example, made in New England, recently was sold for $1,250. The chest-on-chest, the design English craftsmen were making instead of the highboy, was uncommon here but one in maple was recently sold for $1,800.

Lowboys are very much in demand in today's home and are often easier to accommodate in low-ceilinged, post–World War II buildings. The highboy, on the other hand, often appears out of scale in rooms that are eight and a half feet high. The lowboys range from $500 into five figures, with most commanding around $1,000. A particularly fine example in cherry wood sold last year at Parke-Bernet for $6,750.

FEDERAL THROUGH EARLY NINETEENTH-CENTURY STYLES

es After the extremes of eclecticism and of rococo exuberance evident in the Chippendale period, it was apparent that a return to classicism would bring a welcome relief. Neoclassicism had begun in Europe in the 1760's, following the archaeological discoveries made in Pompeii and Herculaneum from 1738 on. As always, there was a lag between the embracing of new fashions abroad and here. The revival of classical design here was delayed by the American Revolution and did not get under way until 1785.

George Hepplewhite was the first to influence the style we now call Federal. The London cabinetmaker, like Chippendale, perpetrated his influence here through the pattern books he published. Hepplewhite's manual, called *The Cabinet-Maker and Upholsterer's Guide,* appeared first in 1788 and was followed by revised editions in 1789 and 1794. Both Hepplewhite and Chippendale

The shield-shaped chair back was one of the most popular in the American ⁌Hepplewhite style. The late eighteenth-century New England chair here has tapering legs with an H-stretcher. *Parke-Bernet Galleries*

were influenced in this period by the neoclassic designs of the great English architect Robert Adam.

In the Hepplewhite period in America, several furniture forms evolved into distinctive designs. Heart- and shield-backed chairs are the most readily recognized designs of the era. But the wing chair, the upholstered settees, arch-backed sofas, sideboards, part dining tables, Pembroke and card tables, tambour desks, field beds and breakfront secretaries underwent other distinctive changes.

Some of the favorite motifs of the era are best seen on the oval-medallion-backed chairs. The American eagle, conch shells, sunbursts, festoons of flowers and other naturalistic motifs were carved to shape the centers of these popular chairs. Inlay work, appearing on chairs, tables, desks and sideboards was another decorative device. But the Federal craftsmen also used japanning techniques; they painted all or parts of furniture, included painted glass panels and plaques on their designs. Where the motif was figurative, there was a tendency to favor musical instruments, festoons of flowers or landscapes with ruins as the themes. Among the most adept at the painted embellishments in the era were the Baltimore cabinetmakers whose work was notable for its elegance and delicacy.

The variations on the carved backs of Hepplewhite chairs again show the increasing ingenuity and skill of American artisans. The evolution of this neoclassic mode in seating designs begins with pierced splats and an arched top

Below: From its circular dished top through its vasiform shaft to its snake feet, this Hepplewhite mahogany candlestand of the late eighteenth century is representative of a furniture form that remains among the most popular today. *Parke-Bernet Galleries*

Above left: The built-in comfort and refinement of the so-called Martha Washington armchair has been copied in all revivals of American Hepplewhite. The canted back, arched cresting, squared and straight legs and canted back legs on this mahogany design made around 1800 are typical. But the ogival arms and down-curving supports add a rare grace. *Parke-Bernet Galleries*

rail. Gone is the horseshoe seat that had lingered into and through the Chippendale period. The lines are squared, with some swelling in front. Legs are straight in front, canted in back and a box stretcher joins them. On armchairs, the rests are open and bowed.

Prices for chairs cover a wide range, but side chairs can still be found at $150 up, armchairs from $200 up. A Martha Washington armchair recently sold for $900, a fair price that for a quality design one must expect to pay.

Settees with shield backs also were made between 1785 and 1800. They had two or three connected shields for backs, seating two or three persons. Longer settees required eight legs for support. Although not so common as chairs, prices are not exorbitant, ranging from $600 into four figures. Upholstered sofas with exposed wood frames also were made with eight-leg supports. They are far rarer in shops and at auctions, and range from over $1,000 into five figures when available.

Dining tables are a specialty of the Hepplewhite style and were developed to a high degree in America. They were made of a variety of center and end tables which when put together extended up to sixteen feet in length. The practicality of such designs was in that when smaller dining tables were required, the end tables were placed against the walls for serving and the center table was used to serve guests. Good tables are not easy to find, and command between $700 and $4,000. A three-part extension table that sold recently at Parke-Bernet brought $900, a fair price for this comparatively rare design.

The smaller tables of the period are very like the Chippendale tables. But the legs are slender and tapering, the tops oval or rectangular and quite often they are inlaid with contrasting woods. The Pembroke, card, lamp and sewing tables are more costly than the Sheraton designs that followed, and range from $200 to $2,500 or more. Three card tables that were sold recently brought $250, $475 and $750. A demilune card table of admirable simplicity was $950. A Pembroke was amazingly inexpensive at a recent sale, bringing $350.

The candlestand is even more common in the Hepplewhite era than in preceding periods. And it also represents when sold possibly the broadest range in price of any table of the epoch. At auction in recent months candlestands of varying qualities sold for the following prices: $55, $175, $200, $225, $250, $375, $2,500 and $3,250. The jump from moderate to fine quality in candlestands is the story in all designs. The finest command exorbitant prices in a booming market, and today's market is commanding higher prices for American furniture than ever before in our history.

The highboy disappeared in this period, and most storage needs were accommodated in chests of drawers with straight, bowed or serpentine fronts. Legs are either short and straight or curved in the Louis XV style. Hallmarks are the cock-beading decorating the façades of chests, oval or diamond-shaped hardware and inlays and carved and curved valances. One may expect to pay $200 and up for chests of drawers. Prices spotted of late show that although some exist tagged at $200 or $275, there is a greater supply of those at $650 or $900, and a few will be offered at $2,000 or more.

Desks are very much like the chests, with the slant-front writing section topping three or four graduated drawers. One might expect to pay $400 to $1,500 for these bureau desks. The secretaries with the two-doored top sections that were decorated with latticework or inlaid with medallions of contrasting wood, bring $800 to $3,000 today.

Tambour desks have many of the same design features as the slant-front designs but are set on higher legs and therefore have fewer drawers. The lighter appearance is balanced by the inlays, the brass medallion hardware on drawer pulls and the enrichment that the tambour gives to the façade. On the distinguished versions by John Seymour of Boston, the neatly fitted pigeonholes are painted blue-green, a decorative treatment favored by this important cabinetmaker. Prices for these secretaries and rolltop desks are generally higher than for plainer types; five figures would not be uncommon to pay for one. The cylinder-front desk is another rare writing design, for which one must pay from $600 to about $3,000 today.

Hepplewhite sideboards, much imitated in the 1920's and 1930's, were made with a variety of façades in the eighteenth century. The serpentine and bow fronts, so common in chests and desks, are repeated in this dining-room design. There are also the so-called half-moon sideboards, named for their semi-elliptical silhouette and the half-moon apron below the center drawer.

Prices for sideboards on occasion will be as low as $225, as one was at a recent Parke-Bernet sale. But most of the designs available range between $600 and $5,000. At recent sales the major portion of sideboards were between $1,500 and $5,000.

The breakfront secretary bookcase, rare though it may be, is available from time to time in shops and at auction. A particularly fine one made in Philadelphia around 1790, embellished by inlays and painted decoration, was the subject of hot bidding at an auction in 1967. Finally it was sold for $25,000.

The field or tent bed, taken from the pages of Hepplewhite's *Guide,* was even more popular in this country than in England from where it came. The arched top, resembling those on tester beds used by army officers of that day, explains the origin of the name. Plain or vase-turned posts frame the bed on designs made long after Hepplewhite furnishings had passed from fashion. Some combine Sheraton and American Empire characteristics. Prices for these beds range from $600 to about $3,000.

Patriotism frequently was registered in furniture details, as in the thirteen stars on the oval American eagle brasses decorating the serpentine façade of this eighteenth-century inlaid mahogany sideboard. The Hepplewhite design on square tapering legs is from Maryland or Virginia. *Parke-Bernet Galleries*

SHERATON

During the first forty years of the nineteenth century, English and French influences on the classical furniture styles produced here, continued in an unmistakable manner. As the century dawned, the straight-legged, shield-backed chairs popularized in London by Hepplewhite and Sheraton, became commonplace in parlors of city and country houses. To these were soon added the Sheraton chairs with crested backs and center panels carved with such other motifs as festoons, foliage, feathers, scrolls, latticework, colonnettes and arch motifs.

The variety of furniture forms was increasing. The sideboard, tambour desk, breakfront secretary, sewing table and half-round card table were introduced in the last quarter of the eighteenth century when the restrained, elegant hand of Hepplewhite was widely emulated in what we call the Federal style here.

Sheraton's contributions in simplifying the silhouettes of Hepplewhite, adding pairs of flanking columns to the fronts of chests, straightening the curved lines of other late eighteenth-century English cabinetmakers and using delicate carving in low relief are immeasurable. He also sparked new furniture forms. To him we owe the early nineteenth-century painted "fancy chairs," those popular designs that Lambert Hitchcock was to mass-produce in his factory

This Sheraton mahogany work table, made in Massachusetts around 1815, has an oblong top with circular reeded corners, threaded stiles topping the reeded, round tapering legs that terminate in ball feet. The old gold damask workbag is accessible when the drawer is pulled out. *Parke-Bernet Galleries*

at Hitchcocksville, Connecticut. And in this period the chest of drawers with attached mirror was developed.

By 1807 the first signs of the Empire style began to appear in the work of Duncan Phyfe, the Scottish-born American cabinetmaker whose strong style would continue to influence the interiors of upper middle-class homes until his retirement in 1847.

But the heavy, ornate Empire style did not fully flower until the 1820's. In the years that followed, French scrolled beds, dubbed "sleigh beds" because of their striking resemblance to the horse-drawn sleighs of the time, began to appear in American homes. Sofas in living rooms sprouted winged lion paw feet. Desks and cabinets stood sentry in hallways and studies or libraries bearing ornate capitals on their façades.

During these years, the Boston rocker was born. The design, which became as American as apple pie, was widely popular through 1850 and was revived in this country for use in living rooms and on the porch. The Récamier sofa, a Grecian-styled, French design that had already been lionized in Paris and London, became a fixture in American parlors in the second quarter of the nineteenth century.

Thomas Sheraton of London wrote two books that were to become the furniture bibles of many early nineteenth-century American cabinetmakers. In *The Cabinet-Maker and Upholsterer's Drawing Book,* published in four parts between 1791 and 1794, Sheraton showed the main differences between his own and Hepplewhite's designs. The former favored more architectural lines—slender, slightly turned and reeded legs, reeded columns decorating the façades of chests, square chair backs, some surmounted by crests. In Sheraton's *Designs for Household Furniture* published in 1812, the French lyre-back chair, carved feet and acanthus motifs—all influences from the French Directoire style—were introduced. That these French elements of furniture design came to us via England shows the dominant influence that Paris had in this period and the continuing importance of English cabinetmakers for their colleagues here.

The recent revival of interest in early nineteenth-century furniture begun in the 1950's became even stronger with the redecoration of the White House by Mrs. John Fitzgerald Kennedy. Mrs. Kennedy chose pieces of the period when the White House was built, a development that sent prices on this previously moderate-priced style skyrocketing.

Sheraton chairs popular in the early years of the century took many forms. Under the characteristic crested top rail, Sheraton and his imitators here did oblong panels carved with delicate latticework and festoon and foliage carving. The carving was noticeably more subdued than that of the eighteenth century. The front legs of chairs were squared and gently tapered, ending in ring turnings. The rear legs canted backward. Seats with squared corners flared wide in front.

Bow-knotted bows and arrows fill the four splats of this Sheraton painted and decorated vermilion and gold settee. The rush seat is bowed in front. Painted musical trophies appear on the crest rail, and leafy decoration is repeated on the seat skirt and front stretchers. *Parke-Bernet Galleries*

Various names are associated with Sheraton-style chairs here. Among them were the crested back, the drawing-book (from the title of Sheraton's book of the 1790's) and the Sheraton armchair. The latter is an upholstered design with exposed concave top rail, open arms ending in scrolls, turned and reeded front legs, and round, canted back legs.

Mahogany was the wood most favored, with some New England cabinetmakers occasionally substituting cherry. Until the recent antiques boom, all such designs found at from $75 to $500 were in relatively good supply. But prices have spiraled upward, and the furnishings have become somewhat difficult to find. One may expect to pay from $150 to $800 for modest to fine period examples of this style.

Fancy chairs were painted black with color or gilt motifs and had ring turnings on front legs. The plain or turned rear legs canted backward and the curved back had a concave top rail. Backs were of plain splats or horizontal bars. Seats were shield-shaped, executed most often in rush or, on occasion, padded and covered with fabric. Such chairs today bring from $100 to $500.

Lambert Hitchcock's painted "fancy chair" bridges the Sheraton and American Empire periods. By contrast with the Sheraton designs, the chair back is a bit straighter and has more turnings in the top rail. Stenciled decoration covers the top horizontal back splat. Front legs have ring turnings, and are joined by similarly turned stretchers. Back legs are turned and joined by uncarved, turned stretchers. Seats are of rush or cane, narrow at the back, flaring wider at the front.

The Connecticut manufacturer produced these painted chairs at his Hitchcocksville factory between 1822 and 1843. Many of those made before 1829 bear a label on the back reading "L. Hitchcock, Warranted," or "L. Hitchcock, Hitchcocksville, Ct." After 1829, the label changed to "Hitchcock, Alford & Co."

Unlike the black Sheraton fancy chairs, the Hitchcock chairs were painted brown-black, to simulate rosewood. The chair was copied widely in other New England factories as well as in New York and Pennsylvania and distributed throughout the Middle Western and Southern states. Although prices have risen on these designs as much as on all antiques, good buys can still be made at from $100 to $300. Of course, the Hitchcock-labeled chairs with their original painted decoration are the most valuable of this genre and will cost more.

The Boston rocker, a cross between the Hitchcock chair and the Windsor, was made in this country from 1820 to 1850. The spindle-backed design had scroll-ended arms and bore the same crested top rail as the Hitchcock. But the entire silhouette is far more curvaceous than the Windsor. The seat starts high at the back, curves down and up again to cradle the knees. The apron on the seat is scrolled and decorated with a stenciled design. The bends of this rocker are short. Most were done in maple, had pine seats, and were painted from top rails to bends to simulate maple or mahogany. Rockers of this type are more available in country sources than city shops and range from $75 to $300.

Sheraton sofas bore straight, gently tapered legs that were turned or had reeded details. The gently curved arms were exposed and the same reeding appeared on them. The many variations of the top rail include a straight enclosed version, a paneled rail that is sometimes decorated with contrasting wood, a carved strip bearing arrows, thunderbolts, drapery or wheat. Many cabinetmakers, including Duncan Phyfe, made such sofas. Adaptations were also produced in the twentieth century, a fact that should make many buyers wary and cause them to examine old ones carefully for the proper construction details. Originals are rare and most are expensive, ranging from four to five figures in price.

Sheraton settees are of two types and easier to find than the sofas. The "fancy" settees are three-seater designs that are like the fancy chairs in triplicate. They are from $300 to $500. The two-seater settees with upholstered seats, urn-splat backs, crested top rails and squared, tapered legs run higher in price, from $400 to $800 or more. The four-seaters run still higher in price. Thus the $550 paid at auction for a fine four-seater decorated with musical trophies, caused some surprise. Most start at that price and climb to four figures.

Like Hepplewhite, Sheraton did part-dining tables. The legs on these newer designs were curved and decorated with foliage, lyres, leaves or animal fur. The tops were rectangular. A small, but extremely fine part-dining table in two parts recently was available for $2,500. Extension dining tables, which gained prominence in this time, cost less. One such brought $750 at Parke-Bernet not long ago. Others are quite likely to bring $1,000 and up.

Above: Three pedestal extension tables for dining continued in popularity from the Hepplewhite through the Sheraton periods. This late eighteenth-century Sheraton table in mahogany has reeded tripod bases on the ends and a reeded tetrapod support under the center section. The paw feet are castered. *Parke-Bernet Galleries*

Right: Contrasting woods used in this New England, circa 1810, card table were a decorated treatment that continued through the American Empire period. Mahogany and cherry are the major woods, and the frieze panels are of bird's-eye maple. Reeded three-quarter round stiles top the reeded round tapering legs. *Parke-Bernet Galleries*

Other types of Sheraton tables—the Pembroke, pedestal-based, and the four-legged card tables—are easier to find. Modest designs come as low as $100, but card tables may well range from $425 and up.

Chests of drawers often have reeded pilasters flanking drawers, and legs that are ring-turned, high and baluster-shaped or plain and reeded. New England chests of this kind are prized for their fine carving and proportions. They may cost from $350 to $2,000. Slightly rarer bow-front chests of drawers with pilasters flanking the drawers and a small upper section containing two small drawers were also made. And flat-front chests on higher legs sometimes come with attached mirrors. The finest of these were made in Salem. Mahogany

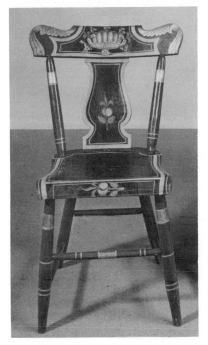

Sheraton fancy chairs were frequently painted with fruit and leaf scrolls. On this Pennsylvania version, the yellow striping to contrast with the simulated wood grain, and the splat back, round legs joined by stretchers and shaped crest rail, are typical. *Parke-Bernet Galleries*

or cherry were the woods favored, and satinwood or other veneers were used for inlays. The range on these is from $500 to $1,500.

Sheraton secretaries are sometimes quite plain, with a fold-over writing flap, drawers below and a cupboard in the top section. They were also made with fall-fronts and surmounted with a molded cornice. Then there were the pilaster-framed designs with a pullout writing shelf, classical arches covering the doors of the upper cabinet and graduated drawers in the base. The rarest of the three types is the simplest and should be searched for in New England antiques sources where prices may range from $500 to $2,000. The other two types, however, may prove more appealing today, and cost from $400 to $1,000. Three sold recently brought relatively modest prices—$275, $300 and $425. A tambour cherry desk went for $475.

Sideboards, whether they had bowed, straight or break fronts, continue to command good prices. Most were of mahogany or cherry with contrasting veneers worked in typical Sheraton inlays. The straight front is the rarest and brings easily $2,000. But others can be had for $175, or for moderate to better quality, $650 or $825.

Sheraton tester beds had slightly tapered and turned posts carved with the usual foliage, festooning, vase or ring turnings. The roofs of these beds were also carved and gilded. Plaques frequently centered the panels of the roof at the sides and at the foot. Headboards were either extremely simple, or conceived as a broken pediment. Most urban cabinetmakers produced the beds, an explanation for the goodly number that appear at every specialized American furniture sale. Duncan Phyfe made some and Samuel McIntire did the carving on some Salem cabinetmakers' beds of the same type. Simple examples can be found for $325 to $1,000, with more in the lower price range than the upper category.

DUNCAN PHYFE

Duncan Phyfe (1768–1854) was born in Scotland and came with his family to this country around 1783, settling in Albany. They moved to New York around 1792. Phyfe was the single most important cabinetmaker in this country during the first half of the nineteenth century. In fact today some authorities have begun to speak of all superbly executed styles popular in this country between 1800 and 1820 as Duncan Phyfe.

But Duncan Phyfe was by nature an interpreter, not an innovator. Through his hands America saw the finest characteristics of the Sheraton, Directoire, Regency and the even more important Empire styles that flourished here between 1800 and the 1840's. The cabinetmaker's skills were so superior that he was able to add many distinctive elements to all these styles, making them distinguishable as his very own.

To his fashionable workshop on Partition Street in Lower Manhattan came New York's finest families to order their furnishings. The variations in his Sheraton-Directoire chairs begin with the turned legs. These were reeded, ending in small-knob feet. Chair backs were decorated with festooned drapery,

Duncan Phyfe incorporated many English and French stylistic details in this mahogany dressing table made around 1820 for his grandniece, Emily Duncan. The uprights framing the mirror and the back legs are reeded. The front legs are carved with leafage and hairy paw feet. *Parke-Bernet Galleries*

The lyriform splat, the sweeping scrolled arms, the reeded uprights and the front legs of hairy animal form ending in paw feet are characteristic of Phyfe's style around 1815, when this chair was made. *Parke-Bernet Galleries*

Although Phyfe was carving saber legs as early as 1807, this mahogany side chair dates from about 1815. The Federal style is further seen in the reeded uprights and seat frame, and the oval slat flanked by leaf scrolls centering the back. *Parke-Bernet Galleries*

arrows, thunderbolts and wheat. Shield-shaped seats were either caned or upholstered. Examples from the master cabinetmaker's workshop bring $800 to $2,000 today. But from his imitators' workshops came designs that now cost from $200 and up.

The curule chair form that Duncan Phyfe revived, differs from the Renaissance Dante chair in that the twin semicircles are under the arms and joined by a turned stretcher instead of under the seat. Made from 1810 to 1820, these chairs now bring prices in four figures and are exceedingly rare.

Amazingly enough, Phyfe had begun interpreting the Regency forms as early as 1807 in his klismos, saber-leg chairs. As the Empire-influenced style developed later, these chairs had sharply curved legs below the acanthus leaf decoration covering the joint on the seat frame. Legs ended in carved or cast brass feet, or, in some cases, ebonized animal claws. The squared rear legs canted backward, and there were no stretchers between, giving this heavy chair frame the lightest possible appearance.

Concave top rails were left unembellished save for some bead molding. But

The innovation credited to Phyfe, as shown on this mahogany card table, is a steel mechanism permitting two of the flaring legs on this table, circa 1820, to swing back, thereby supporting the fold-over top. The metal device is hidden in the central vasiform standard. *Parke-Bernet Galleries*

the center, horizontal splat is centered with a medallion and flanked by scrolls. Arms sweep forward from the back in a downward curve, ending in a scroll and supported by vase-turned, plain or reeded arm stumps. Seats are bell-shaped, covered with caning or upholstery.

Like most of Duncan Phyfe's early chairs, these are of mahogany. And like most of his work, they command high prices and are rare today. One may expect to pay from $800 to $1,500 for a properly identified chair by the cabinet-maker, and from $500 for one by an imitator.

The ingenuity of Duncan Phyfe is demonstrated in his invention of the fold-over topped, mechanical tripod table. He made the design in the early days of the century, using carved leaf detail and routing on the three legs that terminate in animal feet and an urn-shaped central shaft that concealed a steel rod. It was the rod that held the lower leaf to the central shaft and moved the rear legs back when the table was opened. The table is extremely rare and may cost $2,000 to $5,000.

Another pedestal-based design from Phyfe that is equally hard to find and costly is the sewing table with tambour front that sometimes has a lift-up top concealing a writing easel.

The lyre shape that distinguished many of Phyfe's tables also appeared in his mahogany-framed sofas. The motif appears not only as the supports under the curved arms, but also in reversed form; the lyre motif becomes the leg supports. These sofas, too, cost upward of $2,000.

Duncan Phyfe also made the Récamier-like sofa that represented high fashion in Paris, London and New York. Its interpretation generally is done with a curved back, and a double scroll that shapes both the back and the curved arm. Weighty, short bracket legs serve as the underpinnings.

AMERICAN EMPIRE

The American Empire style reigned for more than thirty years in this country. When the fashion began in 1810–15, pieces were marked by far greater simplicity than they would be by the time the style succumbed to the Victorian and rococo revival styles. The craftsmanship ranged downward from extremely fine to poor. The most important cabinetmaker was, of course, Duncan Phyfe. But Charles Honoré Lannuier, a Frenchman born in 1779 who came to New York at the age of twenty-four and worked here until his death in 1819, is also a name to be reckoned with in this period. It was Lannuier who brought a pure French Empire look to this country. His furniture, replete with elaborate ormolu mounts, with superbly carved details, ranks among the finest produced in the time.

This is the epoch of vase-splat chairs. Backs have urn-shaped, vertical supports. Seats are upholstered, solid wood or cane. Top rails may be plain and crested and with rounded ends. The front legs are flat and have reverse ogee curves. The many variations on this theme are impressive, particularly in the production emanating from New England and New York chair factories. A version with the vase splat between two horizontal rails and with a cane seat is known to have been made by William Marcy ("Boss") Tweed in New York City in the years before he gave up his furniture factory and entered politics. Prices for these chairs ranges from $75 to $300.

Armchairs between the years 1820 and 1840 have upholstered backs instead of the carved urn splat. Arms are open, partially upholstered or fully upholstered. Scroll supports support the arms, and legs are either ogee-curved or ring-and-vase turned. Rockers with long bends were also made in this style. Although upholstered pieces are always harder to find than wood chairs, prices should be comparatively low—from $100 to $400 for those that are of moderate to better quality. The finest designs will indeed command more. Rockers, because of their timeless look and continuing popularity, may be higher.

Candlestands continued to be made. Among the small tables of the time, these represent some of the best buys. Examples of from $50 up should be available in shops. They were made between 1800 and 1830 of mahogany, maple, cherry. The better-quality designs will bring between $200 and $600.

Two-part dining tables were still being made in the American Empire period. Like those under Sheraton and Hepplewhite they were designed so that part of the table could be used against the wall as a server. A difference between the early ones and the Empire designs is that the later tables have two instead of three supports. Four legs supported each table and when the drop leaf was raised, a fifth was swung around to support the leaf. The legs are plain or covered with acanthus leaf, foliage or other carving terminating in brass casters.

With dining tables what they are today, small tables are preferred, making these large part tables something of a drug on the market. With luck, such tables can be found for from $200 to $700. Smaller tables with drop leaves, fittings for sewing and other work supplies, for games or for use as consoles, bring far higher prices. A card table with a hinged oblong top, serpentine supports and winged, bird's-head feet recently sold for $800. Similar prices are asked for and received on fine tables, but lesser examples in all types can be found for from $200 and up.

Chests of drawers fall into two basic categories. There are those that derive from the Regency mode in England, and there are those imitative of the French Empire style. Bow-front chests with needed pilasters ending in ring turnings flanking drawers are more Regency in appearance. The Empire-like designs were simpler, framed with columns, standing on animal or S-curved bracket feet. The Regency-like designs can be found for from $100 to $500. The Empire designs are higher—from $200 to $1,000.

Slant-front bureau desks with reeded pilasters on the façade and the enclosed section fitted with tiny drawers and pigeonholes are still to be found in city and country antiques sources from about $300. Secretaries with sloped writing flaps surmounted by upper writing cabinets command from $500 to $1,000 on today's market. The upper section can be identified by the arched or diamond-carved detailing and the simply carved cornices.

chapter 9

VICTORIAN REVIVALS AND NATURALISM

❧ Pioneer collecting of antiques certainly can and will be done in Victorian and later period furnishings. In spite of the fact that the advance guard has already begun investigating certain styles, namely bentwood, Art Nouveau, golden oak and to a lesser extent the revival styles, there is much to be explored and excellent buys to be made.

As with all collecting it is essential that antiques enthusiasts possess more than a cool detachment for their purchases, and more than the attitude that they are making an investment that will pay dividends faster than blue-chip stocks. One cannot live with a fussy, iron centripetal, spring chair for long, unless you love it. Even with spiraling prices on all antiques, there is no guarantee that prices will inflate quickly on late Victorian designs, enabling one to get the same dollar value on selling as when purchased.

The undulating back and the sinuously curved arm, stump, legs and apron on this violet-colored velvet upholstered settee show how cabinetmakers lavished hand skills on mid nineteenth-century furniture. This settee, attributed to John Henry Belter, is a deeply tufted design that was formerly in the collection of Helena Rubinstein. *Parke-Bernet Galleries*

What are the best areas to investigate in the 1850 to 1900 area? Certainly if one is lucky to find the already popular Thonet or other early bentwood and Art Nouveau designs at reasonable prices, they should be snapped up quickly. The designs of Charles Rennie Mackintosh of Scotland, of Frank Lloyd Wright, of Josef Hoffmann of Austria and other turn-of-the-century architect-innovators are just beginning to be discovered. Their architectural-looking furniture stands between that of the arts-and-crafts style of William Morris and the exuberant Art Nouveau era.

But since there is little likelihood that any of these styles will be available at moderate prices, collectors must decide whether to buy fewer, more costly pieces or look elsewhere.

There are other extremely interesting areas to be investigated. The rococo revival will certainly come in the next few years. For those living in areas where the style flourished and retained its popularity through and past the end of the nineteenth century, shops should be perused to make thrifty purchases. Auctions in cities away from New York will certainly yield a harvest of good buys in this field. Strangely enough, New York appears to be the hardest place to find good rococo Victorian furniture. Dealers suggest that Southern cities may be the best place to make purchases.

Judging by the current taste for massive, ornate furnishings, there is also bound to be renewed interest in the Gothic and Renaissance revival furnishings. Purchases in these styles can be made at modest cost today, but five years from now, if the trend continues, these styles will be dearer and harder to find.

Of particular fascination for many collectors today are the specialized areas of mechanical furniture, of nautical designs, of campaign equipment. Certainly the reclining chairs of the late nineteenth century hold a nostalgia—as do the furnishings from old railroad cars, barber shops or dentists' and doctors' offices.

Old nautical chests, chairs and tables from nineteenth-century ships have been back in fashion ever since the boating boom began in the early 1960's. Nevertheless, especially away from coastal areas where this sport has its following, vestiges of the great era of sailing and early steamships may still be found in auctions of ship captains' or their ancestors' possessions.

Also to watch for are the furnishings from the younger sailing vessels—the great twentieth-century ocean liners. The silver-leafed chairs and *art moderne* tables from the old French liner *Normandie*, for instance, would be choice finds today in spite of their youth. Built in the 1930's and one of the most fashionably decorated liners ever to sail the high seas, the *Normandie* had superb furnishings that have virtually disappeared—hopefully into safe hands—to reappear again when fashion or financial needs dictate. The style, although far too young to be classified as antique, is being collected by some as if it were.

Nobody knows how many folding beds and chairs were used in the Civil War, but some have survived, to the delight of collectors in the last decade. Others will surely come on the market at a later date. These metal designs are part of the long history of campaign furniture that has always been cherished by devoted coteries of collectors. Folding chairs for officers would be excellent investments today and as useful in the living room as in the garden—if they could only be found.

The fun and fascination of collecting is, of course, a combination of the delight in the chase and the drama of the capture as well as the education both provide. In spite of the fact that the late nineteenth century is relatively recent, serious scholarship on this period is just beginning. There is little in print thus far that documents the Victorian age to the degree that the Renaissance, French and English eighteenth-century and early nineteenth-century styles have been studied. So there is much for the collector to discover on his own.

All the experts who have begun writing about the years between 1850 and 1900 have been kept busy in the catalogs, the newspapers and the city directories of the period, trying to pinpoint when certain manufacturers were in existence and firm evidence of what they made. Bit by bit the story of such designs as horn chairs is being gathered. This nineteenth-century phenomenon in the history of the decorative arts, it is now believed, began in Austria in the early days of the century. But by the last decades of the Victorian period, horn furniture was being made in England, France, the Belgian Congo and throughout the western part of the United States. This information has been put together from photographs taken by Matthew Brady, antiques dealers' intuition and knowledge of the mainstream styles of the period, from tourist guides and from the examination of extant designs for construction details.

The late nineteenth century offers unlimited opportunity for this type of investigation, something to which amateurs can contribute. Indeed some of the most knowledgeable experts among collectors in any field started with little more than a passion for what they wanted to collect and an intense curiosity to know more about the style.

There is, of course, a great deal that has been documented in museums that now have substantial collections of Victorian decorations. Among the most notable are the Brooklyn Museum; the Henry Ford Collection, of Dearborn, Michigan; Fountain Elms, of Utica, New York; and the Smithsonian Institution in Washington, D.C. Restorations of some of the great Southern mansions of the antebellum period are also being completed and should be visited. The great value of these former private homes is that often they have been restored through information derived from family diaries or through personal knowledge of the family members, which gives us a direct link with the past.

Books are the next most important research tool, especially those with illustrations or those that were written in the period. Reading Edith Wharton's and her co-writer Ogden Codman's discussions of the styles of the late nineteenth century in *The Decoration of Houses,* published in 1897, will give some clues about how homes looked then and some ideas on what tastemakers of that day believed most suitable. A later volume—*Stately Homes in America,* by Desmond and Croly—shows such mansions as that of William Henry Vanderbilt's executed in 1879 and Louis Comfort Tiffany's apartment. The *House Beautiful* of 1878 is another of the many books to be perused for such information.

Actually it is in the nature of the collector to poke and peer into every shop that might possibly contain something they might want to swell their aggregate. Dealers are often a mine of information. Usually when dealers come to know a client well, they are delighted to unburden themselves of the information they have gleaned from more years of looking and handling than most collectors will ever experience. Dealers often know makers' names, curious consistencies and inconsistencies, and variations in materials about particular styles of furnishings.

GOTHIC REVIVAL

The strides made by the Victorians in developing techniques for the mass production of furniture occurred simultaneously with the swelling of the middle class on both sides of the Atlantic. But with few exceptions, the technological achievements of the age remained buried under decorative motifs of the past. Merchants and artisans in their new-found affluence wished to secure their positions in society by adopting the manners and indeed the furnishings favored by aristocrats of the past. By doing so, in effect, they were buying noble ancestry.

The first in a long parade of revival styles was Gothic. It began in the 1830's, but enjoyed its peak more than a decade later. The triple arch, pointed arch, open quatrefoil were often combined with such un-Gothic elements as the spiral-turned or cabriole leg and the cloven hoof. To distinguish these designs from those of the Middle Ages is not very difficult. The latter-day adaptations were never line-for-line copies. The differences are many and as obvious as in architecture. No one would ever mistake the Gothic revival–styled Trinity Church in New York City for Notre Dame Cathedral in Paris. Nor do the pews and benches filling the nineteenth-century American churches look like the choir stalls of fifteenth-century European cathedrals. Gothic revival pews, removed from churches in recent years, have already found their way into

Rosewood neo-Gothic chair designed by Alexander J. Davis dates from 1830. The pointed crest rail, foliage carved at the sides, the play of three arches within the main arch of the back and the hoof-like feet are elements of the exaggeration of the Gothic style popular in the nineteenth-century revival. *Museum of the City of New York*

antiques sources. Prices for these nineteenth-century specimens will be low, $100 or less.

Actually, reviving the Gothic mode was as natural for English furniture producers and architects as updating Italian Renaissance would be for the Italians. For the late medieval mode had never completely disappeared from view in the island kingdom. A century earlier Thomas Chippendale had interpreted Gothic in some of his most memorable designs.

The nineteenth-century romantic writers also helped to spark the revival, as did the publication of several books on the decorative arts. In 1836 Henry Shaw's *Specimens of Ancient Furniture,* the first book on English antique furniture, appeared, showing several Gothic designs. The public was primed for furniture recalling the age of castles and kings.

In America the neo-Gothic style also found champions in the 1830's. Alexander J. Davis, the architect, incorporated rosettes, arches, tracery and heraldic devices in the furnishings he designed for the wood-paneled rooms of his clients' homes. Nicholas Biddle, the statesman, had Thomas U. Walter assist him in designing a small Gothic house on his Delaware River "Andalusia" estate, where Biddle installed the painted white Gothic-styled mahogany bed given to him by Joseph Bonaparte.

Unlike the fourteenth- and fifteenth-century beds on which the design was based, this nineteenth-century bed was garnished with an abundance of arches, had low foot posts and a half canopy instead of a fully-framed fabric roof. The linenfold panels of early beds were ignored by the imitator who created the nineteenth-century copy.

In the 1840's such cabinetmakers as Richard Byrnes of White Plains, New York, and John Jelliff of Newark, New Jersey, became known for their neo-Gothic designs. By the 1850's the burgeoning furniture factories were producing simpler versions of the style. Woods common in the period were mahogany, rosewood and black walnut. They were carved into pointed arches for door panels and chair backs, into spiral turnings on legs, into elaborate moldings with overhang on beds and sideboards. Designs had short bracket feet or plinth bases, tracery and ogee moldings on drawer fronts, and marble or wood tops on bureaus. Many of the chairs had higher than normal backs that were reminiscent of the Gothic choir stalls but not nearly so imposing.

In spite of the style's twenty-year reign, examples are not yet in abundance in antiques sources. Strangely enough, most of the dealers specializing in nineteenth-century styles have thus far avoided Gothic revival pieces. But those offering Italian Renaissance and Gothic designs sometimes stock revival examples. Prices are generally quite low on chairs. Side chairs can be found for as little as $25, but if the upholstery is in good condition, the price may be $150 or more. Armchairs will be $50 or $100 and up.

Cabinetmaker examples of bookcases and sideboards in this style were made up to 1880, and now cost from $300 and up when in good condition or identified as to the maker. Custom-made armchairs, many of which were ordered for churches, meeting rooms and the headquarters of organizations, bring high prices—from $200 to $500 today. Bureaus with spirelike frames for the attached mirrors command from $150 to $500.

ROCOCO REVIVAL

John Henry Belter, like Michael Thonet, was a German-born innovator of the mid nineteenth century. Like Thonet, Belter perfected a method of producing laminated wood furniture, but the two producers differed in every other respect. The bentwood technique that Thonet devised, shaped a new style and pointed the way for assembly-line production of furniture, openly inviting imitation by others.

By contrast, Belter's designs produced between 1843 and 1863 were derivative, harking back to the rococo styles of the eighteenth century. His furniture was expensive and produced in limited quantity for the middle and upper classes. The techniques he mastered, techniques as old as Egypt but ignored for centuries, were kept secret for more than fifteen years. In 1858 his methods became

The rococo revival reached its peak in the period when John Henry Belter reigned as New York's leading cabinetmaker between 1843 and 1863. The laminated rosewood table with its intricately carved and pierced apron, the festoons of grapes and leaves at the base, knees of the cabriole legs and through the stretchers were widely copied by others of the period. This marble-topped table was part of the parlor suite used in Abraham Lincoln's Springfield, Illinois, home. *Henry Ford Museum*

known when he patented the process, but shortly before his death in 1863, Belter destroyed his patterns and wrecked his pressing molds.

Yet Belter's furniture was among the finest of its day, and for many the Belter look characterizes the Victorian mode. He opened his workshop in New York in 1843 or 1844, shortly before Duncan Phyfe retired. The designs Belter produced in his cabinet factory, located toward the end of his career at Third Avenue and 76th Street, were in the Louis XV style. He favored rosewood for most of his production, but occasionally, especially in chairs, he used oak or ebonized hardwood. In rare cases he finished woods with burnished gold leaf.

Rosewood was eminently well suited to the laminating process that Belter developed. Taking quarter-inch-thick veneers that had been planed and sand-papered, Belter soaked them until they were as flexible as fabric. Then layer by layer, until he had built up six or seven layers, he fashioned the chair back against a convex form. Violin-maker's glue was used to bind the layers together. Finally a concave form was fastened with screw clamps to the veneer-and-glue sandwich and slowly tightened during the drying process.

When the chair backs were removed from the pressing molds, further drying was necessary. Then the chair was ready for the elaborate pierced or carved work for which this cabinetmaker was justly famous. Belter lavished roses and lilies, grapes, leaves and scrollwork over the entire chair back or on the borders. His distinctive style of carving was also used on sofas and tables made to match his chairs, as well as on beds, cabinets and secretaries.

From the blossom-carved crest rails on the rosewood child's chair and settees, to their cabriole, castered legs, these seating designs show the weighty and impressive hand of the Victorian Louis XV revival. The chairs, attributed to John Henry Belter, are from the late Helena Rubinstein's collection. *Parke-Bernet Galleries (Taylor and Dull photo)*

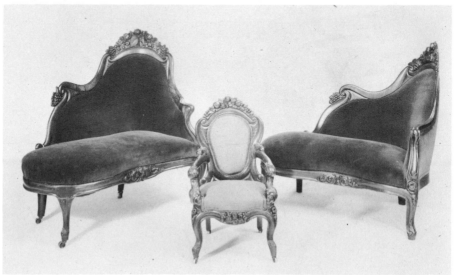

Belter was extremely proud of the strength of his delicately carved designs. He claimed that his furniture was virtually indestructible. In fact, according to one story, he kept a pair of chairs in the window of his second-story office at the Third Avenue factory to demonstrate this claim. Every so often, or so it was said, he dropped one of the chairs out of the window to prove his point.

Today no one would dream of treating Belter furniture in this manner. His designs are prized, and signed examples are extremely hard to find. Until fifteen years ago many of the chairs he made commanded between $75 and $350 when they came up for sale. Inflation in the antiques market has pushed prices of these rococo designs to levels of $500 and up today. Those his imitators made can hardly be found for under $150. A second reason for this change of mind in regard to Belter and other rococo cabinetmakers of the period is the change in the customs regulations governing imports of furniture. The new law, passed in 1966, dates an antique at one hundred or more years old. The old law stated that anything made before 1830 was antique.

But the collecting trend for the dark, brooding mid-century Victorian is just beginning. Within the next few years rococo designs are liable to climb higher in price. Purchases made at small auction houses, privately from families who have owned such furniture for generations, or in shops far from New York City, may net collectors modestly-priced finds.

Belter's designs, although made for the most part for New York families, did end up in distant places. Abraham Lincoln bought a pair of chairs for his Springfield, Illinois, home. These chairs are now in the Henry Ford Museum. Other choice designs are on view in the Brooklyn Museum and the Smithsonian Institution in Washington, D.C.

Among the many American imitators of Belter were Charles A. Baudoine, who is said to have infringed on Belter's patents by forming a bent laminated wood chair back with one difference—a seam down the back. Another cabinetmaker known to have worked in laminated wood furniture was George Henkels of Philadelphia. But the rococo style was favored by artisans throughout the country. Among them were August Jansen, the Meeks Brothers, Alexander Roux, and Gustave Herter of New York; Daniel Pabst and Gottlieb Vollmer of Philadelphia; S. S. Johns of Cincinnati; and François Seignoret and Prudent Mallard of New Orleans.

It is the work of these craftsmen that one hopes to find in shops today. But in lieu of the finer work, it is certainly possible to locate the balloon-backed chairs, the triple-hump-backed sofas and the elaborate marble-topped dressing tables at moderate prices.

Another possible source for those interested in rococo designs is the European antiques circuit. The Louis XV–like designs were at the forefront of fashion on the Continent and in London. Indications are that once the style begins to take root here, antiques dealers will begin scouring sources abroad for their American shops.

Differences between the designs produced here and abroad are many. In Spain, for instance, the dark rosewood and ebonized finishes favored here were disdained. The rococo was executed in mahogany and finished in warm brown tones. Spain has proved to be a favorite hunting ground for dealers in recent years, especially department store antiques buyers. It is quite likely that these departments will be among the first, as they were with Renaissance and with Biedermeier, to show the style.

In France, where the rococo was revived under Louis Philippe in 1830, collectors are already feverishly searching out examples of the style. There is a characteristic restraint in the Louis Philippe designs. Carving is finer and less exuberant than on American designs. Silhouettes are more diminutive and closer to the original mode. The reason for this may well be that the French understood the style better since it surrounded them everywhere, or perhaps the beginning of any revival is far less flamboyant than when it is propelled into high fashion.

There is a major problem with all the Victorian rococo designs. The sofas and chairs, produced in abundance in that day, rarely appear in auctions or in shops, and when they do come up for sale they are often in sad condition. This was the beginning of the great age of upholstery, when more fabric and padding could be seen than chair or sofa frame. Major expenses can be incurred in reupholstering one-hundred-year-old designs. A new fabric covering may increase the price by $100, and if the upholstery must be renewed, the added cost may well be $200 or more.

If the dealer offering such Victorian designs decides to completely reupholster the settees, chairs or sofas, the initial price will be high—from $500 into four figures. One collector who found a horsehair-covered sofa at auction recently for $65, reports that the upholstery was in excellent condition and did not need to be replaced. And the horsehair covering is in top fashion today. He estimated that by using it as he bought it, he had saved himself $300. One reason for the mint condition of the design, he said, is that the sofa is the most uncomfortable he had ever encountered. Probably it will remain in mint condition for another one hundred years,

Parlor tables, clothing cupboards, and chests of drawers from this period sometimes require refinishing. The tables and chests start at $50 and go up to $200 before refinishing and if factory-made, rather than by a known cabinetmaker. Cupboards and wardrobes, especially those that are more architectural in appearance than ornate, cost from $100 to $300.

The Louis XV revival lasted longer than that of any other Victorian style. It began in 1845 and remained in favor up to 1870. It is therefore thought that time will prove what an abundance of furnishings the age produced. The Louis XVI neoclassic revival had a ten-year span, lasting from 1865 to 1875, and never gained the popularity that its predecessor style had.

But like the Victorian rococo designs, the neoclassic revival brought more dark woods and cumbersome furniture into the Victorian home. Black walnut and ebonized local hardwoods like maple were used to fashion the fluted legs that were never graceful, the rosettes, the bead molding, the urn- and vase-shaped finials, the carved masks and the inevitable columns. Everything seems heavy-handed and with little of the imaginative appeal that even the nineteenth-century rococo summoned. Yet a sofa in this style that appeared recently in a New York shop carried a price tag of $250. Bought privately, this same sofa should have commanded $75 to $100. Chairs should be $50 or less, and case pieces would range between $75 and $300.

SPOOL-TURNED FURNITURE

The spool-turned furniture of the mid to late nineteenth century is actually Elizabethan in inspiration. Its importance is that it became one of the most popular styles of the period that was produced at moderate prices.

The spiral-twisted designs, also called "cottage furniture," are this country's answer to European bentwood so far as mass production is concerned. However, the designs produced represented nothing new in technology, as the Thonet bentwood furniture of the same period did. The mass production of these spool-turned utilitarian furnishings was spurred by Lydia Maria Hale of *Godey's*

Spiral-twisted rosewood and mahogany side chair in the Elizabethan revival style, circa 1850, has an elaborately worked foliate back and castered feet. The needlepoint seat is from the period. *Museum of the City of New York*

Spool-turned elm chair, made about 1860, has an adjustable back. The Queen Anne-type cabriole legs show how revival styles were combined without compunction by nineteenth-century furniture producers. *Corner Shop, Macy's, New York*

Lady's Book. In 1849 Mrs. Hale began the "Cottage Furniture Department," a feature in the monthly magazine that offered fresh ideas and line drawings of neat and simple furniture designs. It was in just such a feature that the spool-turned beds, tables, bureaus, chairs and desks were first shown.

Furniture producers quickly saw the value of Mrs. Hale's suggestions, and for the next thirty years they manufactured these designs in abundance. Spool-turned beds proved to be the most popular form of cottage furniture throughout the period. Today these beds range in price from $35 for the headboard alone to $100 for an entire frame. Although not nearly so sophisticated as bentwood designs, the spool-turned production echoed Thonet's point of view—mass-manufactured designs at low cost with interchangeable parts of sturdy construction. The lathe-turned arms, legs, backs, and other parts of these designs looked decorative and represented this concept fully. And although vaguely seventeenth century in appearance, none of the bureaus, sewing tables, dropleaf dining tables, side tables, chairs, stools and ottomans were guilty of the exaggerated pretensions of revival styles of the same and later periods.

RENAISSANCE REVIVAL

The Renaissance revival of the late nineteenth century lasted about fifteen years, from 1860 to 1875 with traces of it lingering into the 1880's. As with all the Victorian revivals, the furniture produced made no attempt to copy earlier designs line for line. Details were exaggerated, and the Victorian love of naturalism blossomed in fruit and floral carvings. Furniture designs, such as the sideboard and the bookcase, unknown in Europe in the sixteenth and seventeenth centuries, appeared in this latter-day Renaissance guise.

Most of the designs that emanated from New York and Philadelphia workshops, derived more from the French and German than from the Italian Renaissance. Heaviness and lavish carving are characteristic. Floral and leaf motifs, medallions, animal heads, and trophy swags swirl in profusion over the doors, drawer fronts, side brackets and pediments. Woods used were black walnut, and, to a lesser extent, mahogany and rosewood. Some pieces bore contrasting ebonized moldings.

The double-decker sideboards have their design roots in French Renaissance *dressoirs*. The base generally has rounded cabinets flanking two center cabinets and topped by four drawers for silver and linens. These dining-room furnishings were often surmounted by ornately carved backpieces supporting a shelf or drawer. Examples can certainly be found in shops for from $100 to $500. Many originals from the sixteenth and seventeenth centuries, surprisingly, do not cost very much more.

Bookcases tended to be simpler than the dining-room furnishings and accordingly command higher prices. Some of these storage units probably were made not only for homes but also for offices. Glass panels were fitted in recessed, double-doored top sections, and wood panels formed the doors covering the base. A cove molding or beveled cornice appeared at the top, and a plinth formed the base support. At estate or city auctions such designs command $200 to $700. Antiques shops specializing in turn-of-the-century furnishings may also show these designs, but the prices may be higher.

Bureaus produced in the neo-Renaissance style were made with their own swiveling mirrors. Some sighted recently in shops carried price tags of about $100 each. Tables of the period, especially the extension-type dining tables with lion-foot bases, are also about $100. The difference between these tables and those of the golden oak era that would follow, is that the Renaissance-inspired tables were more ornately carved, darker in finish, and more imposing in appearance. By the end of the era many families disposed of their dining-room furnishings, selling them for the worth of the lumber, because of their heavy proportions. Those extant extend, depending on the number of leaves, to from six to twelve feet in length.

Center tables may be easier to find in shops. They were made in oval, circular or square shapes, had elaborately carved pedestal bases weighed down with foliage, scrolls, rosettes and animal feet. Today they are available at about $50 and up.

Secretaries, unlike the rolltop desks made for offices and home studies, were ornately carved or had pressed wood embellishments. The secretary actually lingered well past the end of the period into the 1880's. The more restrained late century secretaries range from about $300 to $500.

Then there are the lavishly carved versions that one dealer called "a bad mistake at $85." The Renaissance-style lion-paw feet, the rolling pin pattern just below the cornice and flanking the drawers, the carved patterns on the drawers and further embellishments on the frame might well command $200 in another shop. But that is what makes Victorian collecting such a sport—the inconsistency in price from one dealer to another makes the chase that much more worthwhile.

GOLDEN OAK

The revival of interest in all Victorian styles might well be dated, not to the collecting enthusiasms for bentwood that began in the early 1950's, but rather to the interest in aged golden oak furnishings that erupted in the early 1960's. For it is the golden oak trend that has caused an awakening of interest in the revival styles such as Renaissance and Gothic and will no doubt bring the rococo back into favor.

There are, of course, financial reasons for the switch away from late eighteenth-century furnishings to late nineteenth-century styles. The antiques boom that had begun in the 1950's had pushed prices for French and English designs beyond the budgets of most young collectors. The interior decorators who had helped create the mode for eighteenth-century furnishings by persuading their affluent clients to buy the period, have had little or no influence over today's collectors.

It was the rebellious youth of the sixties, the same young people who changed the clothing fashions, the books and the political issues, who have been buying the late nineteenth-century antiques. The new generation, investigating offbeat shops and auctions, have cast their vote for golden oak. What had been called ugly began to look beautifully ugly or at least useful. Eight years ago the risk in dollars was low enough that there seemed little to lose. Tables and chests of drawers cost $50, chairs $10, and rolltop desks brought about $100.

The rolltop desk holds a special place in the memories of most Americans over the age of thirty-five. These imposing furnishings with their many drawers, pigeonholes, secret corners and most of all their solidity and sense of purpose, were symbolic of a time when it was thought that a man could work out all his own and his family's problems. The office or study that rolltop desks dominated was a sanctuary not easily penetrated.

The rolltop desk was as much a myth as it is now a memory. And today more than a few people want to revive the myth and nurture the memory. Assisting the revival, or because of it, Chet Huntley and David Brinkley, the newscasters, have been shown seated at rolltop desks on their National Broadcasting Company's nightly news show.

In 1959, when the rolltop began reappearing in shops, the idea was being updated beyond recognition by modern designers. The prices for the originals were low—$75 for the smaller designs and $100 for the more imposing ones. The golden oak, walnut and rosewood designs all went for about the same price, with rosewood sometimes edging up to $150 or $200.

The designs now found in shops date to 1885 or 1905. Recently a New York dealer specializing in the period confessed that within one year her top price had risen from $250 to $325 (unrefinished). Refinishing today adds from $100 to $200 to the price and often is well worth the added cost. For in many cases these desks are coated finger-thick with decades of dirt and varnish. Stripping them may be beyond either the amateur's wishes or powers. The smaller roll-top desks, often made for children's rooms or for lower-income families at the turn of the century, bring $75 to $200 today.

Higher prices are generally asked and given for the finer rolltops with hinged sides, secret drawers and brass hardware. Often when a desk has remained in the hands of a single prestigious owner, such as those sold by Morgan & Co. in 1963, this ownership adds to the value and price of the desk.

Chairs used with rolltops were invariably swivel-based, and had seats and backs of wood or cane and bentwood arms. Prices will be about $100 and up on these nineteenth-century relics. One dated cherry-wood chair, its arms bent in a spiral turning, its swivel base in perfect condition, carried a price of $159 in a shop recently. The owner said that if the chair were restored, it would be $250. In some cases such a restoration involves replacing the swivel mechanism from another old chair, mending of the back or seat, new caning or stripping and refinishing.

Although it is hardly thinkable that a shopper would not examine a rolltop inside and out before making a purchase, it has happened. On one occasion a collector was shocked to discover that he had purchased not a desk, but a roll-top lavatory. One must never underestimate the ingenuity of the Victorians.

Revolving oak bookcases, a far cry from the graduated circular designs of the late eighteenth century, are among the most distinctive late-century innovations. Slatted sides on revolving bases formed in medium-height towers make these eminently practical furnishings for today's homes. The display racks for paper-backs in bookstores are made on the same principle. Prices range from $100 to $350, depending on size and condition.

The round dining tables made for homes or restaurants are another eminently popular furnishing of the period. Most could be expanded to banquet size by the insertion of leaves, but in all but rare cases, the leaves have disappeared. Pedestal bases end in claw-and-ball, lion paws or Empire platforms. The demand for this style has been so great, especially in suburban development-type homes on Long Island, that a New York dealer recently commented: "It's a wonder that the island doesn't sink from the weight of the oak."

The major difference between home and restaurant tables is apparent in the way the tops are made. Tables for the home were made with aprons and look more finished. Those for restaurants were generally fashioned from one thick slab of wood. Home tables range from $125 to $175; restaurant designs, from $100 to $150. Some observers believe that the best buys in these tables can be made at city antiques shops where they are available in abundance. In suburban and rural shops, prices are higher.

Another commodity thought to be better priced in cities than in suburban sources is the sewing machine base used to support tabletops. These cast-iron, turn-of-the-century designs cost $12.50 to $15.00 in city shops. In places outside of town they command $17 to $25. But for these designs the price difference is small enough that if the iron design is destined to be used in a suburban home, it might be worth buying it locally and saving the carting or delivery from the city.

Chairs that were used with these round tables are in relatively good supply and represent good buys today. These spindle or splat-back designs were made six to a set. But in most shops only sets of five are usually available. The reason is that the dealer takes one chair and uses it to repair or replace the ailing parts of the five others. Prices range from $100 to $275 per set, with the majority at about $140.

The piano stool is back in the American parlor—not in front of the uprights of yesteryear, but as an extra chair. This design from the 1890's that was a permanent fixture in living rooms up to World War II, offered more entertainment to youngsters who twirled round and round on it until they were dizzy, than the piano it was purchased for. By 1963 the revival of interest was well under way, and W. & J. Sloane in New York, after scouring antiques shops in vain to satisfy customers, was considering manufacturing modern copies. The story was reported in the press and on the day the article appeared fifty people were at the front door of the store before opening time—all seated on their piano stools. Although some sources ask $100 to $200 for these revolving stools, they can be found for from $25 to $50.

CAST IRON

The taste level of the Victorians has been frequently criticized, but their ingenuity is rarely questioned. The metal, particularly cast-iron, furniture they devised is an excellent example.

Metal furniture had been made for centuries. Wrought iron had been used in the Renaissance by Italian and Spanish artisans. In the second quarter of the nineteenth century furniture framed with metal tubing or flattened metal members—namely rockers and later reclining chairs—was fabricated. At the same time English and French blacksmiths began producing wrought-iron garden furniture. These garden designs—the settees, benches, chairs and tables—were probably the inspiration from which American founders cast the less-costly, molded iron furniture.

Cast iron and walnut are combined in this invalid's chair that becomes a bed. Designed by C. B. Sheldon and patented February 1, 1876, the chair was made by Marks A. F. Chair Co., of New York, N.Y., with a ratchet device under the arm to lower the back. *Courtesy of The Henry Ford Museum, Dearborn, Mich.*

The first cast-iron designs for garden use were being manufactured by 1840. In all these and later designs there are echoes of the romantic view of gardening, the wild untended growth of fruits and flowers that ruled the gardens of America and England in the period. The roots of this concept date back to the late eighteenth century, but it took a half century before the idea was accepted widely by the middle classes.

The most popular cast-metal designs were of grape clusters, lilies of the valley, ferns and scrolls. These motifs appeared on round settees that were centered by an ersatz tree trunk and supported by goat's feet. Most of the mid-century examples were not only weighty but were also clumsy in appearance. But occasionally one finds furnishings with swirls of fern-patterned ironwork of unusual and admirable delicacy.

By 1855 cast-iron furniture had moved indoors. Within a short time foundries located in almost every state of the Union were producing curlicued, foliated hat racks, umbrella stands, parlor tables with cabriole legs, mirror frames, fire screens, plant stands and bedsteads. With the exception of the beds and hat racks, all the other designs imitated the currently fashionable wood furniture. Some were even painted to simulate wood.

Victorian iron and wire garden chair, circa 1875, is elaborately if delicately covered with scrolls. But the frame closely resembles the Thonet bentwood chairs of the same era. *Courtesy of The Henry Ford Museum, Dearborn, Mich.*

The most interesting of the iron designs are the bedframes. Early examples show a surprising delicacy. Scrollwork, executed like fine tracery on both the head- and footboards, was the favorite pattern. The beds are similar to wrought-iron designs made in the same period in Spain and France, a coincidence that is best explained by the strong dependence of American artisans on European innovators. American versions are not easily found in shops, and their prices run high—from about $300. The European versions imported by interior decorators and stores in recent seasons command $350 and up. Hat racks in cast iron are about $50 to $150 today.

Iron wire furnishings were also made in the late century. Probably the one design that will survive as a reminder of the fashion is the ice-cream parlor chair, available today from $10 to $25. Children's chairs of wire are far more difficult to locate and more costly. One may expect to pay about $75 for these pint-sized designs.

Iron furnishings offer collectors the opportunity to do some research on the origins of the designs they buy. Most of the cast metal designs bear a maker's stamp and the name of the town where they were made. By checking these names in the city directory of the period when it was likely to have been made, it is possible to narrow down the dating. If the foundry is still in existence, the producer may well have photographs that will explain other mysteries.

PAPIER-MÂCHÉ

Papier-mâché is another of the many materials that Victorian furniture producers experimented with between 1840 and 1870. The molding and pressing machines that had developed home accessories of the material in the early years of the nineteenth century, were commandeered for use in manufacturing full-scale chairs and tables.

The Crystal Palace Exhibition in London in 1851 showed a wide variety of papier-mâché furnishings. Since England led the world in the production of this innovative form of furniture, its appearance at that prestigious show surprised no one. The most noted producer of the period was Jennens and Bettridge of Birmingham. The concern even made a piano of the material.

The papier-mâché center of America was Litchfield, Connecticut, where only a small number of full-scale furnishings are said to have been made. There may have been producers in other areas, but historians believe that most of the paper pulp furniture used in this country was imported from abroad.

Papier-mâché is an extremely durable material made by pressing ground paper pulp or strips of paper together with glue under great pressure. Black lacquer finishes were applied to these finished forms and then gilt or nacré decorations were painted on the surfaces.

Two patents for papier-mâché production were granted in this country, leading some furniture experts to believe that more furniture than we know was actually produced here. In 1772 Henry Clay, a japanner, was granted a patent for molding pasted sheets of soft, porous paper in ovens set at 1,100 degrees. The shaped form was later immersed in solutions of oil and spirits of tar and baked again at 200 degrees, producing a hard product. It was then lacquered and decorated.

The second patent was granted in 1825 for inlaying mother-of-pearl in the material. Other patents were granted later for making larger structural parts.

Papier-mâché furniture is easily recognized by its lacquered finishes and its feather weight. The papier-mâché lacquer designs were in many cases thinner than japanned wood furniture. A tilt-top table would have a serving surface one-half inch thick. A wood tabletop would be three-quarters of an inch to an inch thick.

Aside from the tilt-top designs there were worktables, side chairs and armchairs made of the material for use in parlors or bedrooms. Tables usually had wood bases, but chairs, save the seat rails and sometimes the legs, were entirely molded of paper.

The embellishments on tables were stenciled designs of fruit, flowers and birds, executed in gilt and natural colorings. Chess tables were inlaid with mother-of-pearl. Although not common, these designs are inexpensive, ranging from $100 to $300.

Two types of side chairs were the most popular among the Victorians. Pierced, balloon-backed chairs with U-shaped seats supported on cabriole legs were the most common. There were also solid-back designs edged with scalloped work and with caned or upholstered seats. Both types were richly decorated, sometimes with mother-of-pearl. Made in sets of six or in pairs, few survive as far as can be determined. Even so, designs are not costly, ranging from $75 to $300 each.

Armchairs had scrolled arms and rounded backs and were supported by cabriole or S-shaped legs. One extraordinary example shown by Jennens & Bettridge, called the "Day-dreamer Easy Chair," was described in the catalog of the Crystal Palace Exhibition as being decorated with "two winged thoughts —the one with bird-like pinions, and crowned with roses, representing happy and joyous dreams, the other with leather, bat-like wings—unpleasant and troubled ones." Additional decoration covers the sides and seat rail and virtually every inch that is not upholstered. The chair can be seen at the Victoria and Albert Museum in London. Although armchairs are also scarce, demand is slight and prices should be between $200 and $400.

CHESTERFIELD

In most books on Victorian furniture written to date, the upholstery produced in the period is not dealt with at length. One of the reasons may be that it is extremely difficult to find period examples. In the year 2000, it may well be judged that the Victorians devised the first truly disposable furniture —upholstery.

The importance of Victorian upholstery rests in the technological developments made between 1830 and 1890, as well as in the distinctive forms created. The coil spring shown in Sheraton's *Cabinet-Maker and Upholsterer's Drawing Book* of 1793 did not come into wide use in furniture until the mid nineteenth century. On this development upholsterers built highly distinguished and innovative forms in the ensuing decades. In addition to the springs, there were new ways of tufting devised and new filler materials employed.

The two most important forms developed in the period are the Chesterfield sofa and the ottoman. The Chesterfield sofa, revived about a decade ago, has now been so widely copied that it is rapidly becoming the most popular form of multiple seating in America. These nineteenth-century, plush or leather-wrapped, buttoned-down, rolled-arm and fringed sofas had arms and backs of the same height. They probably owe their existence to the Turkish craze that erupted in Great Britain, Europe and America during the building of the Suez Canal, which was completed in 1869. For it is to the Turks that pillowed, tufted furniture is credited. The resemblance of the Chesterfield to the Turkish divan is unmistakable.

Although some antiques experts dispute this dating, claiming that the design

Leather-covered sofas with swollen arms, deep tufting, pleated details and the height of the arms the same as that of the rolled straight back, are probably a late nineteenth-century development. However, sofas from an earlier period, as this bun foot design made about 1850, were often reupholstered at a later date in the Chesterfield manner. *Philip Colleck*

was in use in the 1830's, most historians believe that the overstuffed design could not have come into being much before 1870.

A few years ago this sofa with a dubious past was thought to have a definite future by a few importers of English antiques. From existing evidence it would appear that these few importers snapped up every sofa or frame that was available in London and environs. Prices started high and have remained there, a matter explained by the fact that these leather-covered designs cost the dealers a fortune to reupholster. Some dealers have the leather hand-tufted and colored after it is in place. Today the range is from $2,500 to $3,000. Copies range from $500 for a machine-tufted product to $2,000 for a design where no frame shows, indicating that there is some truth to what the antiques dealers claim.

The name of the sofa has led some furniture dealers to believe that its origin is earlier than the 1870's. There were two Lord Chesterfields in the late nineteenth century, the seventh and the eighth, and neither of them was particularly prominent in society. So naming the sofas after one or the other of these gentlemen seems highly unlikely. Their ancestor, Philip Dormer Stanhope, fourth Lord Chesterfield, is said to have worn the first Chesterfield coat at the end of the eighteenth century. But the cynical statesmen and author died in 1773 in Chesterfield House, London, about fifty years before the springs used in Chesterfield sofas were developed for upholstery.

No matter where the name comes from (perhaps the town of Chesterfield in Derbyshire, where upholstered furniture was and still is being made), the sofa's position in history is secure.

The so-called Turkish chairs of the late nineteenth century are forerunners of the upholstered designs most favored by interior decorators today. The side chair has a straight, rectangular back, and a pillowed seat fixed to the base. Although the chair has a wood frame, nothing of the wood shows. Corner chairs have rounded, sausage-like backs, diamond-shaped seats and the two back supports of exposed wood showing where seat and back are joined. The extant seating of this period is difficult to find. But prices are not high. The range is $20 and up for arm chairs, $15 and up for side chairs and $50 and up for corner chairs.

The interest in things Turkish included the ottoman and other designs. Ottomans have all but disappeared, but if some old ones are found, their prices would be comparable to the chairs, not the sofas.

BAMBOO

By 1890, sunlight began to penetrate the gloomy interiors of the late Victorian home. It swept through the front hallway where it touched the cast-iron coat rack that had stood sentry by the stairs in a rather forbidding manner for decades. No one knows how many injuries children sustained flying through these darkened caverns, unwittingly encountering the heavy-pronged coat and hat racks of the day. A few knocks on the head in childhood helped to make the younger generation receptive to the rattan and fragile bamboo furnishings by 1890.

The actual introduction of bamboo to replace cast iron began in the 1880's. The bamboo designs were featherlight. Hallstands that looked vaguely Eastlake in style, angular with a suggestion of a pediment on top, were simply framed with two long and two short sticks of bamboo. These bamboo rods supported two cane shelves and a mirror. They were used to deposit calling cards, mail, a visitor's pocketbook or hat. Such stands are frequently shown in shops and should be inspected for repairs.

Plants had moved into the home and appeared there in great profusion by the end of the century. So the bamboo plant stand, still a fixture in the American home, was born. This four-legged bamboo affair had a cane shelf at top for the plant that was often surrounded by a gallery to keep the potted palm from falling off. The base was also equipped with a shelf for a smaller plant or watering can.

Bamboo furnishings were mostly of the accessory type. Seldom were major furnishings made of the material. But overmantels, whatnots, mirrors, small chairs, stools, chaises, tables and small bookcases were produced. These range in price from $35 to $50 for the stools, $125 for the hat racks and $300 for the chaises. A wicker, four-tier bookcase costs about $200 and plant stands command about $20 up.

Rattan has always been with us in furnishings but has become abundant

An 1860 bamboo and lacquer cabinet made in England has
the cupboard doors at the base decorated with Japanese lacquer work. *Philip Colleck*

Two-tier whatnot with a magazine rack in the base
is an 1890 bamboo design with straight legs in back,
bent in front. *Corner Shop, Macy's, New York*

since the mid Victorian period. Actually wicker arrived in this country on the *Mayflower*. The wicker cradle now in Pilgrim Hall, Plymouth, Massachusetts, rocked Peregrine White to sleep after he was born on the *Mayflower* in 1620. In the Victorian era settees were made as early as 1850. And although some historians date the wicker era as 1880, the future may well combine the Victorian and Edwardian designs into one evolving style.

Very little has changed in the design of wicker furnishings over the last century. The curvaceous settees of 1850 are still being made in less fussy versions today. C- and S-shaped scrollwork covers the backs of settees and chairs of the era. Legs were high and gently curved in the Louis XV manner (later they would straighten and still later bow out again). Frames were of steamed and woven cane wrapped over hickory or white oak.

The major difference between the earlier and later modes is that by the turn of the century more designs were made for sun parlors, living rooms, study and bedroom. Chairs and settees in all shapes, some even like Chesterfields, appeared with or without coats of white or green paint. Wicker tables were used to hold magazines or to serve lemonade. The rattan chaise was a fixture in those "outdoor rooms" of past years.

Then, as now, many of these designs emanated from Hong Kong and the East. But they have always had more of a Western than an Eastern flavor so far as their design is concerned.

The rattan headboard remains one of the most popular of these turn-of-the-century furnishings. Hearts, scrolls and floral patterns were worked into the designs. These basic motifs were found, undergoing very little change, in designs from the late Victorian era through the end of World War I. Prices are relatively low—from $50 to about $100 for the double-bed size.

BENT TWIGS AND HORN

Seriousness in furniture design was going out of fashion along with corset stays and hourglass gowns by the end of the nineteenth century. Sunlight had penetrated the front hallway and the parlor. Indeed, the use of glass in homes in that era was a far cry from what we know today. But the small-paned windows were far larger than what the previous generation of homeowners had enjoyed, and a sense of airiness began to penetrate interiors.

People began to think it would be fun to have lightweight furnishings in the garden and on the porch. From there it was a small step before frivolous furniture moved indoors. Actually the porch itself, or the piazza, as it was called, was soon being warmed with the new hot-air heating systems and then glassed in. The development gave us the first twentieth-century family room.

From the 1890's up to World War I there was a new sense of freedom in the materials employed in furnishings. Rockers were fashioned from bent twigs. These designs were probably handmade by the homeowner, handyman or local craftsmen. Economic though they must have been then, they are not so inexpensive today. When first rediscovered by interior decorators operating their own antiques shops about eight years ago, a rocker cost $125. Today one pays $175 to $200. Twig tables are between $50 and $100.

Horn furnishings are another evidence of the late-century vogue for naturalism, not only in form but also in the materials used. Horn furniture is thought to have been made as early as the late eighteenth century, but designs seen in shops today are younger and from three or four sources. There are the Austrian designs from the Biedermeier period employing elk or moose antlers with wood. There are the Scottish designs from the mid to late nineteenth century, some of which were used to furnish a corridor and room at Osborne House on the Isle of Wight, Queen Victoria's sprawling mansion where she died in 1901. And there are the American designs made to some extent of elk horn, but mostly of steer horn. Abraham Lincoln owned an elk antler chair and Theodore Roosevelt owned both an antler and a steer horn chair.

Steer horn furniture, sometimes dubbed "early Chicago stockyard," is probably the most abundant in city shops and throughout the South and Far West. Although chairs are the most common examples, a wide variety of other de-

Naturalism reached new heights at the end of the nineteenth century in such antler furniture as the stag horn chair made in Scotland, the combination stag and elk candle-holder and the elkhorn rack with a wood base from Austria. *The New York Times Studio (by Bill Adler)*

signs were made. Rockers, tables, settees, footstools, mirrors and tête-à-tête sofas have been seen in shops of late bearing price tags ranging from $300 for chairs, $650 for rockers and $25 for footstools.

It is the chairs that have become so popular, possibly as a result of Theodore Roosevelt's cow horn chair that thousands have seen while visiting the gun room at his Oyster Bay, Long Island, estate.

There are a variety of stylistic details that might be checked when shopping for these lethal-looking designs. The origin of chairs with a large star on the front seat rail can be only Texas, and the horn used to fashion the concave legs that look as if they have a case of elephantiasis is generally Texas longhorn. Many of the chairs have legs terminating in brass cups, holding glass casters.

Rockers are also made in many ways, but the platform type is probably the most common. Most experts feel that the longer the horn used to frame a chair, the better the chair. In one rocking chair seen recently, the horn extended from the crest of the chair back, formed the arms and ended in the seat. Each arm was fashioned from three layers of horns, creating a sinuous frame as curvaceous as the rococo chairs of the mid eighteenth century or the Art Nouveau designs of the early twentieth century.

Tables, too, have their distinguishing characteristics. Some imaginative craftsman seventy years ago made a table, fashioning an apron of the pointed end of the horns and creating a completely asymmetrical pedestal base balancing on three concave legs.

If the designs were collected in the last century because of pride in the opening of the West and a delight in hunting, they are acquired today for quite different reasons. Fashionable decorators have favored them. William ("Billy") Baldwin, whose clients include Mrs. Aristotle Onassis, was one of the first to put his stamp of approval on them. Now the fashion has made the style pure camp. Like Tiffany lampshades a decade ago, these furnishings can only become more popular and costly in the years ahead.

Right: Steer horn chair on castered feet is made of Texas Longhorns, is covered in leather and has the star of Texas centering the seat apron. *The Place on Second Avenue, New York*

chapter 10

COUNTRY AND SHAKER FURNITURE

✑ Country furniture of a distinctive character was produced in New England and other parts of this country from the seventeenth through the nineteenth century. The colonization period produced not only a self-sufficient, strongly individualistic and thrifty citizenry, but it shaped talented craftsmen. Some of these artisans hewed furniture from such local woods as pine, maple, birch and cherry. It was their natural instinct to pare away the excessive details of the more sophisticated styles popular in the cities, and to create something that would be durable, simple and eminently suited to the rugged way of life of the farmer, housewright, lumberman, blacksmith, miller, tanner and shop-keeper.

All the styles of rural furniture produced in these periods borrowed from the continental European and English styles of that or earlier periods. Often there was a lag of from ten to one hundred years between the introduction of a style in urban centers and the end of the style in rural areas. A notable example is the Chippendale chairs, which emerged in cities in the mid eighteenth century and died in the countryside one hundred years later. The rural versions had uncarved splat backs and frames and rush seats.

These chairs can be found today in shops in New York and New England and occasionally in Southern states at prices ranging from about $75 to $300 each. The price not only depends upon the approximate date of the piece, which is a very difficult matter to determine in many of these primitively made designs, but also its condition.

Many of the Chippendale chairs and other rural furniture designs shown in antiques shops today look rather seedy. The finishes, which originally were varnish, shellac, oil, wax, paint or absolutely nothing at all, have darkened, dulled or disappeared over the years. And many have been changed with the change of ownership. Painted finishes in early periods included red, yellow, brown, black, blue, green or gray. They were done alone or in combination and sometimes there were patterns. Marbleized, stenciled and freehand painted designs were among the many decorative treatments favored on country furniture. Some chests and cabinets had floral motifs and painted imitations of carving.

Chests are among the best buys in rural furniture today. These storage pieces, often shaped like large boxes or crates, sometimes as simple in their silhouettes as the chests brought over on the *Mayflower*, changed very little from the seventeenth through the nineteenth century. Early settlers fashioned their chests out of local soft and hard woods and then painted them. Details on the origi-

Blanket chest on bun feet in front, peg-like brackets in back, is painted red, has a drawer (not original brasses) in base. The early eighteenth-century design has top and drawers framed by a simple molding. *Richard L. Mills, Exeter, N.H.*

nals, from which they were copied, like the linenfold paneling, the gadrooning, the egg-and-dart motifs, disappeared. The colonists and their descendants simply needed a lidded chest in which to store their clothing or food. Once they settled down permanently on a farm or in a village, they began to decorate their chests, carving scalloped edges or painting designs on fronts and tops.

The results of this evolution produced furniture that is as much, if not more, a part of the American heritage as the work of more skilled cabinetmakers. Some of the earliest examples of folk art and of primitive painting on this side of the Atlantic appeared first on the painted chests and cupboards of the seventeenth and eighteenth centuries. In the Connecticut Valley region and elsewhere, the painted designs on chests with lift-up lids and a drawer in the base often derived from the inlaid wood motifs found on the more formal designs from England and Holland in the same period.

In the late eighteenth century an even more distinctive type of painted design appeared on Pennsylvania German chests. The style is folk art at its most imaginative. Parading across the fronts and tops of these brilliantly colored storage boxes are men on horseback, birds, or an abundance of flowers, sometimes in vases and pots, but often in stylized forms. They are gay decorations, completely symmetrical and often with two medallion-like enclosures on either side of the lock. On larger chests when three patterns appear on the front, the center one differs from the flanking pair.

Carved and painted designs were also done in the seventeenth and eighteenth centuries by Pennsylvania Germans and others. The carving in Pennsylvania designs generally derives from the seventeenth-century geometric-type paneling. The painted designs, however, are far more provincial in concept. Birds, angels

Early writing desks evolved from the Bible box set on a frame base. This Chippendale desk-on-frame in maple and pine shows its ancestry in the lidded box set on a table-frame primitively carved in the mid eighteenth-century style through the apron. *Mary R. Atwood, Roxbury, Conn.*

and flowers are spattered in brilliant colors across the façades and tops of these chests.

In Massachusetts another combination of carving and painted decoration developed a century earlier. Chests with lift-up lids and drawers in the base had overall flat-carved details of tulips, scrolling stems and foliage. Such chests became known as the Hadley chests, after the town where they originated. Some were painted to simulate ebony, and others were finished in red, brown and green. The price tags on these rare designs vary with the quality of the chest and the embellishments, from $700 to about $4,000.

In Connecticut, even more sophisticated decoration was done on the sunflower chests. The upper section below the lift-up lid had incised sunflower motifs and Jacobean ornaments. The remainder of the front had appliqués of half-baluster and knoblike decoration that were stained black again to simulate ebony. These designs are extremely rare, and vary in price from $2,000 to $5,000.

In Guilford, Connecticut, polychromed flowers and foliage and bands of scrolls and leaves covered chest façades. These designs are less costly when found. But they too are difficult to find. One may expect to pay from $500 to $1,500 for such designs.

Hand-lettering was still another form of dressing up chest frames. On dower chests the lettered initials of the owner served as an identification. But other chests were lettered to tell a story using the form of lettering that derived from the illuminated manuscripts of the Middle Ages and was called "fraktur." Originally fraktur denoted a sixteenth-century form of type face, but the Pennsylvania Germans used this term to denote both the lettering and the ornamental motifs that they painted on their furnishings and documents.

The scarcity of most of these early chests may well send most shoppers looking for the later chests of drawers and blanket chests made in the nineteenth century. Pine designs set on bun or peg feet are much more likely to be available within the average person's budget. At country auctions they bring $50, sometimes less, up to $200. The taller chest of drawers commands $200 to $500 or more if the workmanship is fine.

By the nineteenth century modified versions of Hepplewhite and Sheraton four-drawer chests were made and stained to simulate mahogany. Country furniture was losing its individuality as rural areas began losing their citizens to the cities. When the exodus from the countrysides was completed by the end of the nineteenth century, a great tradition in the decorative arts had ended, never to appear again. And in its place was the Sears Roebuck catalog, from which the farmer bought his furniture at prices even he could then afford.

Painted pine settles may have their roots in the medieval choir stalls made for European churches, but on this side of the ocean, these multiple seating designs no longer look or function like their ancestors. The carving is gone and the seat, frame and base are made from planks. The slide-out seat, formerly

Pine blanket chest, possibly late eighteenth or early nineteenth century, is more typical of the kind of storage design found in shops today. The hand-carved chest stands on bracket feet. *Eastern States Antiques Fair*

providing access to the storage place for hymnals, now conceals a cubicle where a colonial housewife kept kitchen utensils, food or linens. Since it was drafty in the log cabins and wood frame houses of settlers, the ears on the European benches were retained to ward off chilly blasts. The settle was in fact the favorite seat placed before the hearth and large enough for the whole family to gather on it.

High-backed settles, produced for more than one hundred years, are returning to popularity in today's homes. Sometimes they appear in the front hall; more often they are used in the kitchen. This seventeenth- and eighteenth-century furnishing in a twentieth-century home may require a few cushions to provide the kind of comfort we have become used to, but otherwise it generally needs little else. Although settles are becoming quite rare, they are not exorbitant in price. Prices range from $400 to $1,000.

Chairs modeled on the high-backed, winged settles were the early colonists' versions of the wing chair that reigned in the parlors of finer houses. Like the two- and three-seater settles, the wood chairs were fashioned mostly from pine, were painted in one or more colors and had in many cases storage compartments in the base. Early versions of these chairs are as elusive as the settles and range in price from $200 into four figures.

The three-legged Pilgrim's chair enjoyed a short reign of popularity from about 1650 to 1670. The design with turned posts and U-shaped arms is so rare that its price is hard to estimate, possibly from $1,000 to $5,000. Wainscot chairs, those heavy echoes of the Jacobean era with solid wood seats and backs, are even rarer and command still higher prices.

A rare and extremely fine Carver chair in maple has the traditional rush seat, single row of back spindles and well-turned finials topping the back stiles. *Putnam House, West Plymouth, Mass.*

Ladder-back chair, circa 1725, is an early maple example bearing traces of the William and Mary style. Back posts are simple round turnings. Front legs end in ball feet. *Courtesy of The Henry Ford Museum, Dearborn, Mich.*

Spindle chairs, called the Brewster chair when it has a double row of vertical spindles in the back and the Carver chair when it has a single row across the back and no spindles under the arms, are available occasionally in shops at from $400 to $700 each. These New England designs in maple and ash had rush seats and are thought to have been made only from 1650 to 1675.

Two reasons for the rarity of these early chairs is that they were not commonly found in middle-class homes, and when they were, there was only one. Although it was reserved for use by the master of the household, it endured hard wear.

With the introduction of the slat-back chair toward the end of the seventeenth century, this practice began to change. Actually over the next two centuries, the slat-back chair became one of the most common forms of seating in the United States. They had three, four or five horizontal slats between turned back posts. Legs were also turned and seats were made of rush. Simple designs were made without finials in every imaginable type of wood, including ash, beech, oak, hickory, curly maple, pine and cherry. Arm, side and rocker versions were made and are still today in such regions as the Appalachian Mountains where craftsmen make furniture by hand as in the eighteenth century. Prices for the more recent examples from the nineteenth century range from about $50; for early examples, one must expect to pay $400 or more.

The Shakers loved this simple form of seating, and from the late eighteenth century on, they put their own stamp on the design, adding finials and a ball-and-socket device under the back legs. The subject is dealt with in greater detail in the section below devoted to Shaker furniture.

The wagon seat is still another form of slat-back furniture. Made for wagons so that family members could ride comfortably, these two-seater designs also were used in the parlors of farmhouses between family outings. They were made with reed seats, and had three upright posts holding two slats for each seat as backs. They were most often rather crudely made of maple, and date from the end of the eighteenth century to about 1825. Prices today range from $100 to $700.

The salamander slat-back, very French in appearance, has turned legs, arms

This early eighteenth-century fiddle-back chair in maple with a rush seat was probably made on Long Island. The turned front and back posts and curved crest rail add distinction to this simple design. *Carousel*

The pierced splat on this eighteenth-century Chippendale chair made in Connecticut shows finer work than was usual in country designs. The curved crest rail and canted back legs indicate that a skilled hand conceived the design. *Rose Olstead, Bar Harbor, Me.*

and stretchers, and was made in New Hampshire and Vermont in the eighteenth century. These are rare slat-backs, a style more common in French Canada than in New England. But they can be found south of the border at from $400 and up. Shop owners generally find it difficult to say whether their offerings are Canadian or American.

Banister-back chairs of the eighteenth century were produced between 1700 and 1725 or so. These chairs show the beginnings of many refinements that would appear in the coming decades in the work of rural artisans. The three to five split banisters were lathe-turned in one of two patterns—vase-shaped or ring-and-ball. Although similar to the Restoration chairs, these banister-backs are also in the earlier tradition of the Brewster and Carver spindle-backed designs. Examples are probably easier to find in New England than elsewhere and fetch between $300 and $2,000.

Some rather offbeat adaptations of Queen Anne and Chippendale chairs were also made in rural areas. These cost $75 to $400 today. Sheraton-type chairs combining Hitchcock characteristics that sell for from $50 to $200 today, as well as rural versions of Victorian revival styles, now costing $40 and up, are also found today along the highways in country shops.

Benches were, of course, a necessity in early homes. They were used around the dining tables and for seating all members of a household in the living room.

Sturdy, hand-carved chair-table, an early and necessary furnishing in colonial homes, is from the late seventeenth or early eighteenth century. Made in New England of maple and pine, it bears vestiges of red paint under the drawer. *Rose W. Olstead, Bar Harbor, Me.*

Benches command a range of prices, from $40 to $400 each, depending on how skillfully they were made and how well preserved they are.

Early joint stools are extremely scarce today. Those encountered in shops are very likely European or English versions. When found, the American ones command $200 and up. Simpler stools like the Pennsylvania footstools made of three planks, or the three- and four-legged stools with round seats, date from the nineteenth century and cost about $35 and up today.

The chair table is one of the most charming anachronisms made in this country from the seventeenth through the nineteenth century. It is part of the ancient tradition of dual-purpose furnishings that comes down from the Middle Ages. In America such designs were economical and space-saving.

The small homes of the colonists necessitated the type of ingenuity that gave rise to chair tables. The table top was round and made of planks. The seat was, of course, of wood set on turned legs or slab sides, sturdy enough to support the tabletop or the sitter. When the table was not in use, it was pushed back to serve as the back of the chair. Some chair tables had a storage drawer under the seat. Prices for these early designs are high, ranging from $750 well up into four figures.

The trestle table is in the same tradition. Two or three plain or simply carved columnar legs braced with slabs of wood at top and bottom form the underpinnings. The tops made of planks were removable in the early period and later became fixed when there was no longer a need to remove the top and dismantle the table after each meal. They were made from the earlier period through the end of the eighteenth century and are available today, depending on size and age, at from $800 to $2,000.

The sawbuck table made of a plank top supported by a pair of "horses" is actually a simple version of the trestle. The design has recently returned to style and is now fashioned from fine woods or chromed metal with glass tops. The origins of the sawbuck are lost in history, but it is believed that it has been made in every country and every period since man first placed a slab on top of a base and called it a table.

The earliest American sawbucks are said to have been made by Swedish settlers in the Delaware Valley. In the eighteenth century, however, the sawbuck was made throughout New England and Pennsylvania. Most often it had a two-plank top and a base of maple or other hardwood. The pine top measured from five to eight feet in length, and from thirty to thirty-six inches wide. Chamfered edges distinguish the eighteenth-century sawbuck from later tables. Although used in kitchens or for dining in the main room of early houses, the sawbuck actually has other uses in barns, stores and elsewhere. Today such tables can be found for from $100 to $900.

The tavern tables of the seventeenth and eighteenth centuries were, of course, not found in homes. But today they are. These small, rectangular or occasionally round tables were made in pine, cherry, walnut, and maple. The pine tops were frequently painted and had one or two drawers directly below the top. The legs and stretchers were turned, showing the last vestiges of the William and Mary style. Later tables took on the characteristics of Queen Anne in their tapered legs and pad feet. Some even assumed the look of Windsors. The simplest versions today are among the most in demand to serve as end tables in living rooms. Late or crude examples are available at from $100, but early designs will bring $500 or more.

The gateleg table was another space-saver in early homes. Leaves dropped down, legs swung in, and a table used to dine on or work at shrank to half its size. Gatelegs were made in many shapes and sizes with oval, round or rectangular tops. Legs were plain or baluster-shaped. Its demise came when butterfly tables with wedgelike leaf-supports and tables with insertable leaves came into being at the end of the eighteenth century. Gatelegs today range from $300 to $2,500.

The butterfly table appeared in the early eighteenth century and enjoyed brief popularity. Only small tables generally employed the pivoting, swing-out leaf-support that was shaped like a butterfly or fashioned in simpler wedge forms. The base of the butterfly table is very like the joint stool and probably was its origin. Few appear to be available; and when they do come up for sale, they command $1,000 or more.

Drop-leaf tables that were country versions of the eighteenth-century formal styles—Queen Anne, Chippendale and Sheraton—are becoming hard to find also, and range in general from $400 to well into four figures. The same can be said of the tray-top, sideboard, tea and gaming tables. Occasionally one does find tilt-tops, with and without birdcages, painted or plain, ranging from $500 to $1,500. Tilt-top candlestands were far more numerous in their time and are in ours, and cost from $100 to $600.

The fold-over Hepplewhite tables were made as game tables for middle-class and country homes in the early nineteenth century. A sufficient number appear to have survived at prices that will not scare collectors. About $100 to $600 is the range for simple examples.

The plainness and sometimes the crudeness of workmanship does not always lower the price on early designs. In some cases the primitive quality adds to its appeal. In the case of these Hepplewhite designs simplicity becomes a virtue. The uncarved legs taper from a shaped apron to the floor. The two-board top has rounded corners. Whether made in cherry, maple or birch in workshops in New York, New Jersey, Pennsylvania or in New England, they have a tendency to look pleasantly alike.

Sheraton tables with turned and tapered legs and oblong or round tops, were made from 1820 to 1835 in even greater quantity and range from $75 to $450 in price.

Cupboards were another fixture in the earliest settlers' homes. The original cupboards were, of course, boards for cups and nothing more. The addition of

Country cupboard made around 1830 is a New Jersey example in pine. The upper cabinet is fitted with butterfly shelves, and the lower cupboard has a shelf with slots for pewter spoons. The LH door hardware is believed to have been salvaged from an early colonial house or furnishing. *Carousel*

Earlier two-piece cupboard fashioned in American cherry around 1750 has
champfered corners above and below, small paned-glass door framed by simply
carved pilaster decoration. *Carousel*

shelves, a frame, and finally doors to partially or completely conceal the contents from view, had occurred by the time the first cupboards were made in the colonies around 1660.

Cupboard bases with two or three doors were used to store food or dishes and utensils. The top had a food preparation or serving surface. Above, and narrower than the base, were open or enclosed shelves to hold pewter and earthenware plates, pots and mugs. Prized examples of these early cupboards with wooden hardware and enlarged scallop-patterned sides were made through the early nineteenth century. They came with or without paint and are mostly of pine.

The Dutch-type cupboard—or *kas*, as it was called—was made in the Hudson Valley. It was, like its European cousins, decorated with fruits and flowers. But the American designs, instead of being carved with apples, grapes and pears, as in the mother countries, were painted in grisaille, or tints of gray. These outsized furnishings stood six feet high or more, generally had two doors enclosing the front, a simple pediment at the top, and plain bracket feet.

Possibly the most popular cupboard today among enthusiasts of country American furniture—and their numbers are legion—is the corner cupboard. Collectors are fortunate, for the style was popular from 1675, when it is thought to have been introduced here. Most of those that do come on the market, however, were made after 1740. The reasons for the corner cupboard's popularity among the colonists are the same as those today. A corner furnishing takes less space in a room than a rectangular cupboard. The dining rooms of yesteryear, when the furnishing was first devised, were certainly no larger than today's small rooms.

Because of the numbers available, the simple corner cupboard has not experienced the same inflation in price as the more formal, rarer examples of colonial furnishings. They can still be found at from $300. But the finest examples are $2,000 or more. Open-faced dressers are about the same price, and closed dressers, which are generally more refined in appearance, range from about $500 to $3,000. Hutches, those cupboards with small doors and ventilated fronts, are not seen often in shops and when found probably carry price tags in four figures.

In spite of the moderate prices on these cupboards, antique shoppers often find only the base or only the top at the same prices. The theory behind this pricing is that the collector will be happy to have either part in this booming period for all antiques.

The dry sink is another extremely popular furnishing among those who covet early country furniture. But contrary to public opinion, the dry sink is of nineteenth-century origin. Most of them are from 1840 or later. Introduced for kitchen use, this pine design with two doors at the base had a copper-lined sink and a drawer. Prices today range from about $100 and up.

Hooded hutch or cupboard with open shelves in the top section, a closed, rather than ventilated, section below, is a charming late eighteenth-century New England example of the country style. *Carousel*

222

Late eighteenth-century maple wall cupboard, of generous size and some sophistication in the cornice carving and brasses, stands on shaped bracket feet. *The Hudson Shop, Inc., Red Bank, N.J.*

SHAKER

Shaker furniture has been aptly and vividly described as "religion in wood." The Shaker Society, a separatist communal celibate sect, was founded in the late eighteenth century by Ann Lee, an English Quaker. These dancing "Shaking Quakers," as they were once called, flourished in America from 1780 through the mid nineteenth century and gave to this country its first original designs. Even today, Shaker furniture remains the single, most powerful creative force in our decorative arts heritage. The greatest influence of Shaker can be seen in modern furniture produced here and in Scandinavia from the 1930's through the 1950's. Their philosophy of design, as indicated in a Shaker saying— "Every force evolves a form"—anticipates the Bauhaus philosophy of the late 1920's—"Form follows function"—by a century.

What is it about the Shaker designs produced in New England and the Ohio area that sets them apart from other country furniture produced in the same period elsewhere in America? Indeed the Shakers made ladder-back and swivel-based, spindle-back chairs. They made kneehole desks, tripod-based tables, stools, drop-leaf and trestle tables. They built architectural furniture into walls, and fashioned a great many special-purpose worktables. Many similar types of furnishings were being produced elsewhere in cities by such cabinetmakers as Duncan Phyfe and on farms by the anonymous craftsmen of the period.

Shaker furniture is notable for its simplicity, as can be seen in the ladder-back arm and side chairs, the tripod table, the spinning wheel and the eminently practical wall cupboards. The collection is in the home of John S. Roberts, Shaker Farm, Canaan, N.Y. *The New York Times Studio (by Gene Maggio)*

A Shaker bedroom was usually equipped with peg moldings on the upper walls on which the chairs were hung during cleaning. The beds were on casters. Washstand shows its Hepplewhite and Federal ancestry. Collection of John S. Roberts. *The New York Times Studio (by Gene Maggio)*

But if the basic types of Shaker furniture designs are not unique in form, everything else about them is. Unlike most country furniture of the period, Shaker furniture is of consistently fine quality—both in the curly maple, cherry, and pine woods chosen and in the execution. In spite of the diversity of forms, you can spot Shaker furniture almost immediately in a shop filled with other designs. This is furniture showing the natural grains of woods, or in some cases, stains or paint delicately applied to surfaces.

Every piece has a rare proportion, grace and refinement. Rodlike uprights on the ladder-back chairs are topped with acorn or knoblike finials. Arms on chairs are shaped, never carved. The square lines on chests are softened by tapered legs. Wood knobs are used for drawer pulls.

The Shakers were an ingenious bunch. They developed or invented tools and devices for bettering farming (a sidehill plow), building (cut nails), gardening (packaged garden seeds), and homemaking (the clothespin). In furniture they developed the ball-and-socket device at the base of the rear legs of side chairs, which permits the sitter to rock or tilt without wearing out the carpet.

The use of large wooden casters on beds is also attributed to the Shakers, as is the application of drop leaves to tables, counters and walls. Lining walls with pegboards and building furniture into walls are other innovations for which they are responsible.

Although there have been avid collectors of Shaker furniture for many decades, the general public did not become aware of the virtues of these designs until the mid 1950's. At that time ladder-back chairs could still be found for a few dollars, chests for under $25, and desks and beds for from $50 to $200.

But these prices, as with all antiques, especially of American origin, have risen sharply. Shaker ladder-back chairs command from $100 to $200 (higher if there are arms). The rockers made for the aging or invalids, were ladder-back chairs with bends and large flat knobs at the ends of the arms that fit right in the palm of the hand. These are from $200 up today.

One charming desk found in the shop of a Shaker dealer recently was distinctive for its low height and small proportions. It was one of the many made-to-order designs for a short deaconness. The kneehole desk emanated from Hancock, New Hampshire, and carried a price tag of $1,600. In the same shop a Shaker six-board chest of drawers was about $175; a painted, lemon-yellow sugar chest that opened from the top and could be used today as a small blanket chest or possibly in place of an end table, was $275.

Shaker furnishings rarely come up at city auctions and are best found in antiques shops in the areas where the community flourished. New England has many such shops, and in New York State the Shaker enthusiasm among dealers and young collectors is increasing annually. And so are the prices.

GLOSSARY

GLOSSARY

Acajou Mahogany (in French).

Acanthus Leaf A stylized ornamental detail derived from the leaf of a prickly plant found in the Mediterranean region. It was used from antiquity and in most classic revivals as in the Renaissance and Empire periods.

Acorn Finial A cone-shaped ornament on chair stiles, as in the Shaker period.

Anthemion A flat, carved, or painted floral ornament usually of a honeysuckle-like flower, derived from Greek classic decoration.

Applied Cresting A carved crest piece attached to the top rail of a chair or sofa, as on Victorian furniture.

Applied Ornament A carved or lathe-turned decoration attached to the façade or top piece of a piece of furniture.

229

APPLIQUÉ   A French word meaning an ornament affixed to a furniture surface.

APRON   A panel-type extension or skirt of a chair or table frame that appears directly below a tabletop or chair seat and connects the legs or stiles.

ARABESQUE   An intricate pattern of interlaced lines using floral, geometric, foliate, or figural forms in painted, inlaid or carved decoration.

ARCADED   A series of arches carved in low relief with or without columns or piers and used to decorate a cornice frieze.

ARCHED MOLDING   An uncarved half-round convex molding used singly or in pairs on many parts of furniture, usually in classical styles.

ARCHITECTURAL FURNITURE   A large piece that has architectural elements worked into the surface, or which, by its shape and decoration, appears to be built into or designed for a particular room.

ARCHITRAVE   A decorative band framing the door or other opening on furniture.

ARM PAD   An upholstered pad on a chair arm which became a prominent feature on Louis XVI and later styles. In French it is called *manchette*.

ARM STUMP   The support under the arm on a chair that replaces the upward extension of a front leg.

ARROW SPINDLE   A slender shaftlike rod, carved on one end to resemble a sharp head, that was used on the back of Windsor chairs.

ASTRAGAL   A beadlike molding camouflaging the joining of double doors in secretaries and cupboards.

BACK STOOL   A term for an early chair that was armless and had a stool base.

BAIL HANDLES   Drawer pulls in half-arch shape, usually of brass, and anchored at either end in attached posts.

BALL FOOT   Round furniture support, usually of ample proportions and used mostly on such large pieces as chests and cupboards.

BALL LEG TIP   A small brass or glass ball-shaped furniture support held by a cup or claws that function like casters on a table or chair.

BALL-AND-STEEPLE   A turned spirelike finial set on a round base.

BALUSTER   A vertical member, usually turned and vase-shaped, that is topped by a rail. It is also called a banister. Balusters appear in chair backs, table and chest bases, or cut in half lengthwise as surface decoration on cupboards.

BAMBOCCI   Italian chest-desk of little drawers.

BAMBOO TURNED   Describing a furniture element or frame with ringed detail to resemble the joints in a stalk of bamboo.

BANDING   A narrow border framing a drawer front or other furniture panel. Sometimes it is an inlay or an applied decoration in metal or a contrasting wood.

BANISTER   A corruption of the word *baluster,* a banister is a lathe-turned splat used in a chair back.

BAROQUE   Any design that is irregular in form. Or, specifically the style of art and architecture developed from the late sixteenth into the eighteenth century

Louis XVI bergère
Richard V. Hare

William and Mary baluster framed chair
French and Company

in Europe. It is characterized by dynamic tension and by the use of curved and contorted forms.

BARREL CHAIR   An upholstered chair that is usually shaped like a half-cut cask.

BEAD AND REEL   A round convex molding composed of disks and knobs.

BEARER STRIP   A strip of wood at the bottom of a drawer opening, supporting the drawer front when closed.

BERGÈRE   An upholstered armchair that is closed under the arms. It derived from the French word for shepherdess. The bergère first appeared under Louis XIV, but was perfected in the Louis XV period.

BEVEL   The slanted edge of a board or panel cut to reduce the thickness.

BIBLE BOX   A small chest with a hinged flat or sloping lid used for reading or writing and for storing books and writing materials inside. It originated in the seventeenth century or earlier.

BIRDCAGE   On a tilt-top table, the double-block cagelike device located under the table top, permitting it to tilt and to rotate.

BLANKET CHEST   A case piece, also called a mule chest in England, that has a hinged lid, deep well and one or two drawers beneath. The name "blanket chest" is American, derived from the furnishing's primary use.

Block Foot A cube-shaped foot capping the end of a square untapered chair or table leg of the Chippendale period. Also known as Marlborough foot.

Block Front A paneled façade of a chest or secretary on which the central panel is sunk between two raised side panels. It was popular in the Chippendale period.

Bobbin-Turned Describing spoollike turned wood used as frames or appliqués on furniture, especially in the late nineteenth century.

Body-Conforming Shaped to the human form, as the seats of Windsor chairs and the backs of Queen Anne chairs.

Boiserie A French term for woodwork; used to designate eighteenth-century carved wood panels covering the walls.

Bolection A bold projecting curved molding framing panels on chests, doors, . or the openings of fireplaces.

Bombé The French term for a rounded, convex or bulged front and sides of a chest, commode or secretary, commonly appearing on baroque or rococo furniture. It is also called a kettle base.

Bonnet Top A broken arch top with the split extending the depth of the top of the highboy or secretary. This hooded detail was popular on eighteenth-century English and American furniture.

Borax Cheap and showy furniture that was originally sold by premiums in boxes of Boraxo, a cleaning compound.

Boss A small rounded or oval appliqué on the surface of furniture.

Boulle A decorative inlay technique developed by André Charles Boulle, the elder, setting tortoiseshell or brass in scroll and cartouche motifs in seventeenth- and eighteenth-century furniture. In England it was called "buhl."

Bow Back A Windsor chair back on or in which the bow or hoop is continuous either down the arms or the seat.

Bow Front The convex-shaped façade of a case piece.

Bow Top The curved top rail on the back of a chair.

Box Stretcher The square or rectangular base of a table, chair or chest formed by square or turned members.

Bracket A shaped support that reinforces the angle formed by two structural members on a piece of furniture such as the leg and seat rail of a chair or the leg and sides of a bed.

Bracket Foot An extremely simple, plain or scrolled furniture support used under mitered or rounded corners on chests, cupboards or secretaries.

Braganza Feet The Spanish or carved scroll feet used in the William and Mary period. It derives its name from Catherine of Braganza, the Portuguese wife of Charles II.

Breakfront A large case piece, such as a bookcase or china closet, that has the top set back from the base, thus interrupting the continuity of the façade.

Brewster Chair An American colonial chair with two tiers of boldly turned posts in the back and decorative spindles above and below the seat and arms.

It derives its name from William Brewster, American colonist and one of the leaders of the Pilgrims.

BRITISH COLONIAL   A furniture style developed by British settlers in the West Indian, South African, and Indian colonies in the late eighteenth and nineteenth centuries. The highly functional, consistently simple late Georgian designs, including officer's chairs and chests, show local influence in design and materials.

BROKEN PEDIMENT   The triangular element crowning a tall case piece on which the curved or slanting parts do not meet at the apex.

BUFFET   A dining-room furnishing, also called a sideboard, that was used to store or display tablewares. The buffet was highly developed in France and in England in the Stuart period and later in many forms throughout the Georgian era, both in Europe and America.

BUN FOOT   A slightly flattened, round furniture support or footpad.

BUREAU   Originally, "bureau" meant the cloth cover for a table used when writing. Later, "bureau" came to mean a table with a small chest on top used as a desk. In eighteenth-century England the term came to designate a desk with drawers or a secretary. In the nineteenth century the word began to be used in America for a chest of drawers used in the bedroom.

BURL   Figured, mottled or speckled veneer, cut from an excrescence on a tree trunk.

BUTTERFLY TABLE   An evolution of the medieval joint stool, this small table has drop leaves, legs angled outward, and an oval top. The drop sides are supported when open by butterfly-wing–shaped brackets.

CABRIOLE   A leg with outcurved knee, incurved ankle terminating in an ornamental foot. The term originated in Italy to designate a representation of the rear leg of a leaping goat.

CAMELBACK   A double-curved chair back, in shield shape, characteristic of Hepplewhite furniture.

CAMEO   A raised delicate carving on stone or imitation stone used to decorate furniture in the Sheraton, Adam, and Empire style.

CANAPÉ   A French word for a sofa or couch that was originally curtained with mosquito netting.

CANE   Split rattan woven into the seat and back of panels of chairs and settees.

CANNELLATED   Fluted or channeled, carved, or molded detail, as on furniture legs or pilaster appliqués.

CANOPY   The framework or roof of a four-poster bed that is frequently covered with fabric. It is also called a "tester."

CANTED   A slanted element on furniture, such as chair legs angled backward.

CAPITAL   The carved uppermost portion of a column or pilaster on a furniture façade on which rests the top of the chest or cupboard.

CARCASS   The basic framework of a piece of furniture before embellishments are added. Specifically, it means the frame of a case piece.

CARREAUX Flat cushions placed on the floor for seating in eighteenth-century French houses.

CARTOUCHE A furniture ornament carved or inlaid, usually in a scroll or oval tablet shape.

CARVER CHAIR An American colonial chair usually with a rush seat and three vertical and horizontal spindles at the back. Its name derives from John Carver, first governor of Plymouth Colony, who owned one such chair.

CARYATID A carved ornamental draped female figure used as a support usually on the stiles of Italian Renaissance chests.

CASE PIECE Any boxlike furniture design such as a chest, bookcase, or cupboard.

CASSAPANCA An Italian Renaissance settee created by adding arms and a back to a chest. The term means *cassone,* "chest," plus *banca,* "bench." The base is used for storage.

CASSONE A rectangular, boxlike Italian chest of ample proportions which has a hinged lid and decorated façade.

Florentine sixteenth-century cassone
Parke-Bernet Galleries (Taylor and Dull photo)

CATHEDRAL SHAPE A pointed arch in tracery on a bookcase, and the chair backs of the late eighteenth- and nineteenth-century English and American Gothic revivals.

CAUSEUSE A French two-seater sofa with open sides.

CAVETTO A concave, quarter-round molding used to trim the edge of a table top or other furniture part.

CERTOSINA Mosaic inlay of bone or ivory in a dark-wood field, worked in geometric, crescent, triangular, or star patterns, indicating that the technique may be of Mohammedan derivation.

CHAISE À CAPUCINE A turned open armchair or sidechair with a straw or rush seat in French provincial furniture.

CHAMFER   A planed or cut surface where two furniture parts meet. The technique disguises the joint.

CHIFFONIÈRE   A tall, narrow storage piece, like a chest of several drawers, used mostly by women in France. In America it is usually a bedroom furnishing.

CHINOISERIE   A style of European decoration partially in imitation of the Chinese decoration but also including Western elements.

CLASSICAL ORDER   The term designating the arrangement of structural supports in ancient Greek and Roman architecture and furniture design. Below the columns or pilasters are the base moldings, and above are capitals and entablatures. The order was also used in the Renaissance and in later neoclassic revivals.

CLAW-AND-BALL   A carved furniture foot shaped like a bird's claw holding a ball. It is commonly used as the termination of a cabriole leg by Chippendale.

Claw-and-ball foot
Parke-Bernet Galleries

CLOVEN FOOT   A leg termination cleft in two or more parts favored in eighteenth-century England and in continental tables and chairs.

CLUB FOOT   A knobby leg termination resembling the head of a cudgel. The leg swells to the stubby ending and stands on a thick flat base. It was popular on eighteenth-century furniture.

COCK BEAD   A diminutive, half-round applied molding that projects past the edge or façade on furniture.

COCK'S HEAD   A type of hinge shaped in the form of the European herb that has small spiny-crested pods and is called a cock's head.

COFFER   A chest with a hinged lid used to store and transport money, jewels, linens, utensils and valuables. The trunk usually was flat on top, making it suitable for seating.

COIL SPRING   A heavy wire spiral used in upholstery from the late nineteenth century down to today.

COMMODE   The French word for a chest of drawers. In the nineteenth century the word also designated a movable washstand with a cupboard underneath.

CONSOLE   A table attached to the wall with two front legs that in French derives from the word meaning "bracket."

Louis XV console
Parke-Bernet Galleries

CONVOLUTE   A twisted or scrolled configuration.

CORBEL   A bracket-like projection serving as a support in architecture or in cabinetwork.

CORNER BLOCK   A brace of triangular or other block shapes supporting the joints of legs and seat rails on chairs and sofas.

CORNER CHAIR   A chair designed to fit into the corners of a room, with its seat set at a diagonal, four legs under each of its corners, and a back of splats and three spindles. Also known as a roundabout chair.

CORNICE   The crowning horizontal projecting molding or group of moldings on a piece of furniture.

COUCH   Originally a bed or furnishing for sleep but now a sofa with a raised headrest, back, and sides.

COURT CUPBOARD   A two-section cupboard with an upper cabinet closed behind two doors and an open base less often closed with drawers or with doors. It was popular in the sixteenth and seventeenth centuries in England and America.

CREDENCE, CREDENZA   A cupboard or sideboard of the Renaissance made of oak or of walnut. It was used for storing dinnerware and displaying the plates. From the French word for "belief," *credence* originally referred to a table for tasting foods or drink to determine if they were poisoned.

CREST RAIL   The carved or painted top rail of a chair, centered by an armorial or other design.

CRESTING   The ornamental carving on the top rail of a chair, on a base stretcher, pediment, or uppermost part of a mirror frame.

CRICKET   A low wooden footstool, in early English furniture, that was also copied in colonial America.

Tuscan sixteenth-
century credenza
French and Company

CRICKET TABLE In Jacobean furniture, a three-legged round table, measuring about thirty inches in its diameter.

CROMWELLIAN The furniture period 1649–60, named after its central figure, Oliver Cromwell. The furniture of this time is a severe undecorated version of the Jacobean out of which it grew. Squarish silhouettes, ultra-simple moldings and ornaments, and austerity rather than comfort characterized the style in England and in Colonial America.

CROSS MEMBER A structural horizontal framing element joining the sides of chests or uprights of chairs.

CROSSRAIL A horizontal slat in the back of a chair, joining the sides or stiles.

CROSS STRETCHER An X-shaped brace set horizontally at the base and connecting the legs of chairs, tables or case pieces.

CROTCH GRAIN A veneer cut from the main tree crotch or the part of the tree where two branches meet. Generally the term referred to mahogany veneer.

CUP TURNING An inverted bowl turning used in William and Mary furniture.

CUPID'S BOW A bow-shaped top rail commonly found on Chippendale chairs.

CURULE CHAIR In Roman times, a seat for those in highest office. Generally then, and later, a folding base of curved legs. Curule chairs of the Renaissance were called Dantescas.

CYLINDER FRONT A desk or secretary façade in curved form equal to one quarter of the cylinder that opens to reveal the work area.

CYMA-CURVE A wavelike profile, half concave and half convex.

DANTE CHAIR (DANTESCA) A folding X-shaped chair of curule form of the Italian Renaissance. Seats and back were usually leather slings stretched between the sides of the frame.

DAVENPORT The term derives from the English word for "a small desk." But

Dante chair
French and Company

in contemporary Amercan use, a davenport is a large upholstered sofa that doubles as a bed. A davenport table is one used behind a sofa.

DEMILUNE From the French for half-moon. A half-round console table or other furnishing.

DENTILS A series of toothlike carved embellishments projecting below a cornice.

DIAPER PATTERN A repeating design of lozenges, squares, diamonds, and related shapes which connect or evolve from each other. In Gothic art, diaper patterns were carved on furnishings.

DISHES Concave depressions on tabletops to hold plates.

DIVAN A large backless, sideless low couch that originated in Turkey. Today the term refers to almost any couchlike piece of furniture.

DOVETAIL A type of joining in furniture shaped like a dove's tail.

DOWEL A rodlike pin that fits into two parts of a piece of furniture, fastening them together.

DRAKE FOOT A three-part clefted termination of a cabriole leg that is turned outward like a duck's foot. Also called a Dutch foot or trifid foot.

DRESSOIR An open framework or shelves to display china and tablewares, developed in the Gothic period in France, Flanders, and the Germanic countries. Later in England and Wales the upper part was open, the lower part enclosed. Also called a dresser or a combination buffet-cupboard-sideboard.

DROP A turned pendant hung from a furniture member.

DROP-FRONT A hinged writing-desk surface that opens downward when it is put in use.

DUCHESSE In French, a kind of chaise longue in one, two or three parts, one of which is like a gondola-back chair.

DUMBWAITER A portable serving stand of three or more tiers used to carry plates, food, and papers. Usually it had a central shaft and a tripod base.

ÉBÉNISTE The French word for an expert cabinetmaker, derived from the ebony furniture makers of the seventeenth century, then called *huchiers*.

EBONIZED Wood finished by paint or stain to imitate ebony.

EGG AND DART An egg-shaped molding alternating with another in the form of a dart.

ENCOIGNURE A diminutive French cabinet or chair designed to fit into the corner of a room.

ESCRITOIRE A writing table equipped with drawers and organizers in Georgian England.

ÉTAGÈRE A multi-shelved cabinet, larger but similar in use to a whatnot, that is open on all sides.

FALDSTOOL An early English curule-type folding stool, chair, or desk at which one knelt in prayer.

FALL-FRONT A hinged writing flap of a desk or secretary that opens downward.

FANBACK Spindles of a chair back spread fanwise from the seat to the top rail, especially on the Windsor.

FARTHINGALE CHAIR A broad-seated armless chair popular in England in the reigns of Elizabeth and James I. So named because the fashionable wide dresses called farthingales determined the design of this armless chair.

FAUTEUIL French upholstered armchair, the sides of which are open, while the sides of the bergère are closed.

FESTOON A carved or molded applied decoration shaped like a rope or like a garland, chain, or wreath of flowers.

FIDDLEBACK The violin-shaped solid splat of a chair, characteristic of the Queen Anne period.

FIELD BED A canopy bed planned in the seventeenth century to be portable. Later it meant modest beds with curved canopies and low posts.

FILIGREE An open or closed decorative design of extreme delicacy, imitating intricate wirework.

FINIAL Any crowning detail on the back stiles of a chair or at the corners or center of a cornice on a chest or secretary. The shapes may be acorn, ball, steeple, urn, or vase.

FLARE The widening at the front of a chair seat from a narrower back.

FLEMISH SCROLL A carved ornament of two S-curves that meet at right angles, used in Flemish sixteenth- and seventeenth-century designs and in William and Mary furniture.

FLUTING Carved or molded vertical channels or furrows on a columnar element. It is the opposite of reeding.

FOLIATED Leaflike carving or other ornaments.

FRAKTUR From the word designating a style of German type, it is a term commonly used for Pennsylvania German hand-lettered illustrated manuscripts and artwork.

FRETWORK   Decorative openwork or relief carving consisting of small and straight lines or bars intersecting each other at oblique or right angles. Sometimes it is in foliated scroll patterns.

FRIEZE   Any sculptured or ornamented band on furniture, as beneath a cornice or below a tabletop. In the latter sense the frieze is the same as the apron.

GADROON   A carved design of elongated ovals bordering table edges, cornices, and bases of furniture.

GALLERY   Brass or wood railing edging tables or shelves.

GATELEG   A drop-leaf table with legs that pivot out to support the hinged leaves.

GESSO   A plaster of Paris or gypsum mixture applied to a woodlike surface to fill pores, especially where the surface is to be gold-leafed.

GLAZING   Providing with or fitting door frames on cabinets or bookcases with glass panels.

GOUGE CARVING   A notched carving cut by a chisel; also called nicking.

GRILLE   A grating, usually of metal, used on cabinet or bookcase doors. Patterns are varied. Curtains are often used behind the grille.

GRISAILLE   A gray monochromatic painted decoration on wood cabinets and tables or on glass.

GROTESQUE   A carved or painted decoration showing human or animal forms surrounded by foliage, flowers, fruit, or wreaths.

GUILLOCHE   Interlacing bands of ornament leaving circular forms which are filled with round motifs or disks.

HADLEY CHEST   An Early American chest, with a hinged flat lid and drawers in the base, made in and around Hadley, Massachusetts. Most were embellished with carvings and the owner's initials.

HANDKERCHIEF TABLE   A drop-leaf table that is square when open but triangular when closed, thus fitting in corners. The triangular leaf is the same size as the triangular top.

HERRINGBONE   Decorative pattern, sometimes inlay, fitted together to resemble the spine of a herring.

HIGHBOY   A high chest on tall legs comprising two sections of drawers. In England it was called a tallboy.

HUTCH   Derived from the French word *huche,* it is a chest or cabinet with doors, usually standing on legs.

INCISED CARVING   Ornament created by cutting into a surface.

INLAY   A decoration of wood or metal set into the surface of a piece of furniture.

INTAGLIO   A motif forced below the surface of a material which gives the opposite effect of relief decoration.

INTARSIA   Wood inlaid in contrasting wood as the ornament on furniture.

JACOBEAN   A decorative arts style in England covering 1603 to 1688. It parallels the Renaissance, but the forms are simpler and lighter.

JAPANNED English word for imitative lacquer used as a finish on furniture. It was similar in effect to that used in the Orient (thus the term) but far less costly.

JOINT The part linking two members in the structure of furniture.

JOINT STOOL A stool made by a joiner with a flat seat, four splayed legs, and stretchers in between.

KAS A large Dutch-style cupboard often bearing painted floral decorations.

KETTLE BASE A rounded front on furniture. The English term for a bombé front.

KIDNEY TABLE Dressing or writing tables in an oval shape with a concave front.

KLISMOS A Greek chair form with concave-shaped back following the curve of the human back, and curved legs.

KNEADING TABLE A bread trough, oblong in shape, resting on short legs, used in the provincial areas of Europe.

KNOB-AND-RING A lathe-turned finial with rounded shaping above one or two elements of disklike design.

LACQUERED A shiny and smooth finish created by colored opaque varnishes on metal or wood. The finest work was done in China and Japan. The term derives from lac resin, the substance achieved after crushing, washing and purifying lac, a resinous substance secreted by an Indian insect. Japanning is imitation lacquerwork.

LADDER-BACK A chair with a back framed by two uprights joined by horizontal slats, as the rungs of a ladder.

Chippendale ladder-back,
New Hampshire, 1780
*Courtesy of The Henry Ford Museum,
Dearborn, Mich.*

LAMINATED WOOD   Thin layers of wood glued together, now called plywood. In the nineteenth century both Michael Thonet and John Belter used laminated wood on furniture.

LATTICEWORK   A crisscross pattern of lathes or thin bands of wood, or a carved imitation of the effect so achieved.

LAZY SUSAN TABLE   A revolving circular tray surmounting a table intended to hold plates. It also means a muffin stand.

LINENFOLD   A carved decoration imitating fabric or draped hangings. This Gothic treatment probably originated in the Middle Ages in imitation of the folded napkin on the chalice.

LIT CLOS   The "closed bed" built-in or free-standing in rooms, common in French provincial furniture, particularly in Brittany.

LOOP-BACK   A rounded chair back formed by a single piece of wood bent in a loop and fastened to the back ends of the seat. In Windsor chairs, the loop-back is also called a bow-back or balloon back.

LOW-BACK   A type of Windsor chair with a combination arm and top rail in one continuous bow shape. The spindles under the rail were short and thus the name.

LOWBOY   A nineteenth-century designation for the earlier kneehole-type dressing table similar to the lower section of a tallboy, as it was called in England, or highboy, as it came to be known in America.

LOZENGE   A diamond-shaped pattern.

LUNETTE   A carved or inlaid crescent or half-moon element in a decorative design.

LYRE   A classic decorative design shaped like the stringed musical instrument framed by two curved uprights, a straight bar across the top, and curved element at the base. Used for chair backs and table bases.

MARBLEIZE   To affect the look of marble by paint or stain.

MARLBOROUGH LEG   A squared leg often ending in a plinth foot used in English Chippendale and many American styles.

MARQUETRY   Inlaid work in wood of contrasting wood or other materials.

MARQUISE CHAIR   A completely upholstered, extra-wide bergère armchair derived from the French for a marchioness, the wife of a marquis.

MEDALLION   A relief carving or painting on a panel, centered or applied to a piece of furniture and resembling a large medal. Medallion motifs may be figural, portraitlike, or geometric.

MELON FOOT   A vertically grooved bun foot used in English furniture.

MENUISIER   A French word for the joiner and his work and the carpenter and his work. The term for cabinetmaker, *menuisier en ébéne,* means a joiner specializing in ebony wood.

MÉRIDIENNE   A French Empire daybed with outscrolled ends at different heights connected by a shaped back.

MOLDING   A narrow band either flat or rounded, sunken or projecting, finished with decorative embellishments and applied to many parts of furniture.

Louis XV marquise
Parke-Bernet Galleries

MORTISE A hole into which a tenon fits joining two parts of a piece of furniture in what is called a mortise-and-tenon joint.

MOSAIC Surface decoration made by inlaying bits of wood, glass, stone, in patterns pictorial in nature.

MOUNTS The ornaments and hardware applied to furniture. Usually the term refers to the edgings or protective elements, as the gilt bronze mounts on cabriole legs that served as guards for the knees.

MUDEJAR The term applied to the art and architecture that merged Mohammedan and Christian elements in Spain between 1250 and 1500.

MUNTIN The wood sash bar holding glass panes in doors or windows.

MUSHROOM-TURNED Designating umbrella-shaped knobs with flatly curved façades.

NEOCLASSIC A revival of classical taste and style including the Renaissance, Adam, Louis XVI and Empire styles.

NEST OF TABLES A late eighteenth-century English innovation in which three or four tables fit one inside of the other.

NOTCHING A primitive form of decoration by cutting into small hollows.

OGEE A reversed-curve molding, carving or outline, as the pointed Gothic arch.

OGIVAL Formed like a pointed arch, as in Gothic architecture.

ORMOLU Metal gilded with ground gold. From the French *or moulu*. The same as bronze *doré*.

OTTOMAN   A backless upholstered seat, couch, or footstool, so named for its Turkish origin.

OVOLO   A curved convex molding, often embellished with egg-and-dart or gadroon motifs.

OXBOW FRONT   A compound curved façade, found on Chippendale and other styles, that is concave at the center and ends, convex between. It is the opposite of serpentine.

OYSTERING   Oval-shaped veneers cut as cross sections of roots and branches of some trees, resembling oyster shells and used as inlays. It was a favorite device of the English designers from the end of the Jacobean period to the end of the seventeenth century.

PAD FOOT   An oval-shaped termination on cabriole legs.

PALMATED   A petallike ornament, used in a running series on Stuart furniture.

PANETIÈRE   A spindle-framed cupboard that probably originated in the Provence region of France, and was used for livery.

PAPIER-MÂCHÉ   A substitute for wood or metal in furniture, made by molding a paper-pulp substance that is mixed with size, glue, rosin clay, and other elements. The French term means "chewed paper."

PARCEL GILDING   A partly gilded design on a carved or flat surface in early eighteenth-century English furniture.

PARQUETRY   An inlay in wood of contrasting-colored wood of geometric or other pattern.

PASTIGLIA   An Italian Renaissance treatment in which a carved surface was covered by thin fabric, covered with plaster (*pastiglia*) in several steps, and finally gilded.

PATERA   A small, round, and flat dishlike ornament applied to friezes, chair splats, and mirror crestings.

PATINA   The mellowed look in color and texture of a furniture surface. It is caused by age or use.

PEDIMENT   The triangular top surmounting a tall piece of furniture. Often the profile is broken at the center or is scrolled in shape.

PEMBROKE TABLE   A small drop-leaf dining table standing on four squared legs. It was fashionable in mid to late eighteenth-century England and America.

PENDANT FINIAL   An embellishment in acorn, urn, or vase shape, attached to the apron of a table, chest, or chair to hang downward.

PIECRUST TABLE   A round tilt-top table of the Chippendale period or style, with a raised and fluted edge resembling the crimped edge of a piecrust.

PIER GLASS   A tall, skinny mirror placed on the so-called pier section of a wall between two windows or two doorways, often with a pier table at its base.

PIETRA COMMESSA   Marble inlaid with marbles and stones in floral, foliate, bird, and scenic patterns.

PIETRA DURA   An inlay of small, fine stones, used in tabletops, especially of the Italian Renaissance period. A finer form of inlay than *pietra commessa*.

George III Pembroke table
Parke-Bernet Galleries

PIGEONHOLES An open letter- or paper-file in a desk or cabinet.

PILASTER A structural pier in architecture or stile in furniture with a capital at top, shaft and base, that looks like a column.

PLAQUE Any thin ornament of wood, metal, clay, or ivory inserted in the surface of furniture.

PLINTH A base of a piece of furniture without a molded edge which rests directly on the floor.

PLYWOOD Layers of wood glued together so that the grain of any one ply is at right angles to the grain of the next.

POLYCHROME Many-colored decoration on furniture and in the arts.

POUDREUSE A powder table, usually small. An oblong-topped vanity with the top divided into three hinged sections. The two end sections open outward and are fitted with shelves. The center has a lift-up mirror and fittings below for bottles and toiletries. From the French *poudre,* "powder."

PRESS CUPBOARD Like the English court cupboard, the American press cupboard of the seventeenth and eighteenth centuries was a large rectangular piece with one or two doors, drawers and bulbous legs.

PRIE-DIEU A desklike furnishing with a kneeling platform at the base and a space below to store the prayer books. Also a high-backed chair with a seat low enough to kneel on.

PRINCE OF WALES PLUMES The three-ostrich-plume emblem of the Prince of Wales used by Hepplewhite as a chair-back design.

QUATREFOIL A four-leafed flower or cluster of four leaves used in Gothic art as a carved or pierced decoration.

Rabbet A rectangular slot, channel or groove to receive another member like a panel. Also called "rebate."

Rail A horizontal bar between two furniture parts, as an arm or top rail on a chair.

Rake A perpendicular angling of a chair leg or back.

Récamier A French daybed or couch with both the head and foot end of equal height and scrolled outward, introduced in the Directoire period. The name derives from the painting by Jacques Louis David showing Madame de Récamier on such a daybed.

Reeding Parallel lines of beading popular on furniture between 1790 and 1830. It is the reverse of fluting.

Refectory A long, narrow table used originally in a dining hall of a monastery or convent, called a refectory in the Renaissance period.

Rent Table An English eighteenth-century round or octagonal pedestal table with filing drawers in the sides used for a landlord's collection of rents.

Riband Back A Chippendale chair in the French taste with a splat of two long C-scrolls interlaced with ribbons and surmounted by a bow and tassel.

Rocaille An eighteenth-century style of embellishment utilizing elements resembling the imitation rockwork and pierced shellwork of the period. The French term *rococo* evolved from "rocaille."

Rococo A style of unsymmetrical ornamentation characterized by curves combined with shells and rocks. "Rococo" is derived from the two French words *rocaille,* meaning "rockwork," and *coquille,* meaning "shell."

Rolltop A desk with a sliding tambour cover made of horizontal wood strips glued to a flexible backing.

Roundabout Chair. See Corner Chair.

Saber Leg A perpendicular curved slender leg shaped like a saber, used in late eighteenth- and nineteenth-century furniture.

Savonarola An X-form chair of wood slats of the Italian Renaissance.

Sawbuck A table with trestle ends in a cross- or X-shape.

Scroll A curved ornament that may resemble a paper furl and be S-shaped or twisted.

Seaweed Marquetry Inlay worked in interlacing designs suggesting marine plant life. It is prominent on seventeenth-century English furniture.

Secretary Generally, a desk with an enclosed upper section for books and drawers below its fall-front writing surface.

Serpentine Front A compound curved façade on a case piece chair or sofa that is convex at the center and at the ends, and concave between. Oxbow is the opposite.

Settle A high-backed wood bench with arms, seating two or more and equipped with a closed base designed for storage.

Sgabello A wooden sidechair with an octagonal seat and two slablike wood front and back supports instead of legs. It was popular in the Italian Renaissance.

Queen Anne slipper chair with
square seat
Parke-Bernet Galleries

SHIELD BACK   A late eighteenth-century English chair associated with Hepplewhite, made with pierced splat or having banisters framed in a shield form.

SKIRT   The bottom cross member, sometimes also used to designate the apron, the panel below a chair seat or tabletop.

SLIPPER CHAIR   A bedroom chair with short legs on which a person sat to put on his slippers.

SLIP SEAT   An upholstered seat in a wood frame that is designed to be taken out of the chair when necessary.

SNAKE FOOT   An elongated foot shaped like the head of a snake, used on cabriole legs.

SPADE FOOT   A quadrangular foot terminating a tapered leg that looks like a spade. It was used by Hepplewhite and Sheraton.

SPANISH FOOT   A carved scroll foot with vertical ribs used instead of the bun foot in the William and Mary period.

SPINDLE   A turned rod or slatlike member in a chair back.

SPLAT-BACK   A solid or pierced upright back support on a chair.

SPOOL-TURNED   Designating turning for stiles, legs, stretchers and appliqués on furniture in ball, ball-and-ring, bobbin, knob, sausage, urn, and vase shapes.

SPOON-BACK   A chair back gently curved to match the curvature of the spine, the most notable example of which is the back splat of the Queen Anne chair.

STILE   The upright element in framing, for example, the chair back uprights or the vertical front elements on a chest.

STIPO   A drop-front Italian Renaissance cabinet desk.

STRAPWORK   In decorative design, a narrow fillet or band folded, crossed and sometimes interlaced.

Queen Anne spoon-back chair
Parke-Bernet Galleries

STUMP LEG   A plain, squared back leg on a chair that has a slight backward cant.

SWAG   A wood or metal decoration that is carved or cast to imitate festoons or folded draperies.

TABORET   A low upholstered footstool introduced in eighteenth-century France.

TALLBOY   A tall chest-on-chest wider at the bottom than at the top. The term in England corresponds to a later American designation of the same piece, the highboy.

TAVERN TABLE   A small table set on four turned legs, with an oval or oblong top and an apron below, which was made for eighteenth-century inns and tap rooms.

TENON   A tonguelike wood part that fits into a hole in another furniture part to make a mortise-and-tenon joint.

TENT BED   A small four-poster bed resembling a tent, with a curved, low canopy.

TÊTE-À-TÊTE   A short upholstered canapé or sofa for two persons, especially so they face each other.

TILT-TOP TABLE   A circular, square, or octagonal topped table that tilts and stands on a tripod base.

TRACERY   Carved or molded openwork, like that of a Gothic window, used to decorate furniture panels.

TRESTLE   Support like a sawhorse for a tabletop. Trestles are usually mounted on a block, or on shoe feet. In the Middle Ages through the mid eighteenth century, trestle tables, often with removable tops, were used for dining.

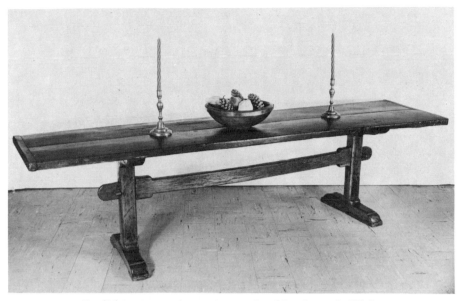

English seventeenth-century trestle table. *Gertrude Weber*

Louis XVI tric-trac table. *Philip Colleck*

TRIC-TRAC   The French word for backgammon and the table it is played on.

TRIFID FOOT   A triple cleft; sometimes known as a drake foot.

TROMPE L'OEIL   A decorative treatment to fool the eye. Painted or inlaid details that look three-dimensional.

TRUMEAU   The French word for a pier mirror used over a console or commode and frequently decorated with a painting at the top.

TURNING   The rounded or trumpet, ring-and-ball shaping of a leg or other furniture part, usually executed on a lathe.

URN   A sculptured classical decoration resembling an urn, used frequently as a finial.

VARGUENO   A Spanish Renaissance cabinet desk with a fall front.

VENEER   A thin layer of fine wood glued on one of inferior wood.

VITRINE   A glass display case for curios, china, and small art works.

VOLUTE   Coiled, rolled, or scroll-turned element on almost any part of furniture.

WAGON SEAT   A crude Early American settee on a frame, used in a wagon or house. Some had splint or rush seats, but most were merely wood.

WAINSCOT CHAIR   A heavy oak chair notable for the solid, sometimes carved, panels on its back and slab-wood seat. Originated in England, it was widely used in Colonial America.

WELSH DRESSER   An oak dresser with open shelves above the surface where foods might be prepared or dressed and with closed cupboards below.

WHATNOT   A small piece of furniture with shelves for displaying collections of objects. It was popular in Victorian parlors.

Georgian oak Welsh dresser. *Parke-Bernet Galleries (Taylor and Dull photo)*

WHEEL BACK   A carved or spindled chair back in a shape resembling the spokes of a wheel.

WHORL FOOT   A termination for a cabriole leg in a curved scroll shape.

WING CHAIR   A large comfortable chair with padded earlike side pieces at the top of the back. Called an easy chair in late eighteenth-century England and America. It probably evolved from the earlier French "confessional" chair.

X-CHAIR   An ancient type of chair shaped like an X. It was known in Egypt and Rome, and appears in the Middle Ages. The Dante chair of the Renaissance and the modern director's chair are X-chairs.

BIBLIOGRAPHY

⇝ This bibliography has been compiled with a special emphasis on works offering strong or unusual visual presentations or comparative studies of historical styles and social causes of the periods covered. Further study may be made by consulting the bibliographies of the works cited below. All Parke-Bernet catalogs covering furniture offered at auction from 1964 through April, 1969, were studied, but for lack of space are not listed here.

ARONSON, JOSEPH. *The Encyclopedia of Furniture*. New York, 1938.

BOGER, LOUISE ADE. *Furniture Past and Present*. New York, 1966.

————, AND BOGER, H. BATTERSON. *The Dictionary of Antiques and the Decorative Arts*. New York, 1967.

BUCHWALD, HANS H., ed. *Form from Process—The Thonet Chair*. Cambridge, Mass., 1967.

BUTLER, JOSEPH T. *American Antiques 1800–1900*. New York, 1965.

CARTER, JACK, ed. *Thonet 19th Century Bentwood Furniture*. Los Angeles, 1961.

COMSTOCK, HELEN, ed. *The Concise Encyclopedia of American Antiques*. New York, 1965.

DAVIDSON, MARSHALL B., and the editors of *American Heritage*. *American Heritage History of Colonial Antiques*. New York, 1967.

DREXLER, ARTHUR, AND DANIEL, GRETA, eds. *Introduction to Twentieth Century Design*. New York, 1959.

GLOAG, JOHN. *A Social History of Furniture Design from 1300 B.C. to 1960 A.D.* New York, 1966.

LYNES, RUSSELL. *The Tastemakers*. New York, 1949.

NICKERSON, DAVID. *English Furniture of the Eighteenth Century, Pleasures and Treasures*. New York, 1963.

OGLESBY, CATHERINE. *French Provincial Decorative Art*. New York, 1951.

ORMSBEE, THOMAS H. *Field Guide to American Victorian Furniture*. Boston, 1952.

———. *Field Guide to Early American Furniture*. Boston, 1951.

PEDRINI, AUGUSTO. *Italian Furniture, Interiors and Decoration of the 15th and 16th Centuries*. Florence, 1948.

PRAZ, MARIO. *An Illustrated History of Furnishing*. New York, 1964.

SACK, ALBERT. *Fine Points of Furniture—Early American*. New York, 1950.

SCHWARTZ, MARVIN D., ed. *Please Be Seated: The Evolution of the Chair, 2000 B.C.–2000 A.D.* New York, 1968.

SELZ, PETER, AND CONSTANTINE, MILDRED, eds. *Art Nouveau: Art and Design at the Turn of the Century*. New York, 1959.

VANDAM, CHARLES, ed. *Great Styles of Furniture—French, English, Italian, Dutch, Spanish*. New York, 1963.

WANSCHER, OLE. *The Art of Furniture, 5000 Years of Furniture and Interiors*. Copenhagen and London, 1966.

WHITON, SHERRILL. *Elements of Interior Design and Decoration*. New York, 1957.

WILLIAMS, LIONEL H. *Country Furniture of Early America*. New York and London, 1963.

WILSON, PHILIP, ed. *Art at Auction*. New York, 1968.

INDEX

INDEX

257